FOR ORGANS, PIANOS & ELECTRONIC KEYBOARDS

E-Z PLAY® TODAY

296

56 STANDARDs

MW00804406

ISBN 0-7935-0556-9

A
Belwin, Inc.
CPP
PUBLICATION

Exclusively Distributed by

Hal Leonard Publishing Corporation

7777 West Bluemound Road P.O. Box 13819 Milwaukee, WI 53213

C O N T

E   N   T   S

All I Do Is Dream Of You

Registration 2
Rhythm: Swing

Words by Arthur Freed
Music by Nacio Herb Brown

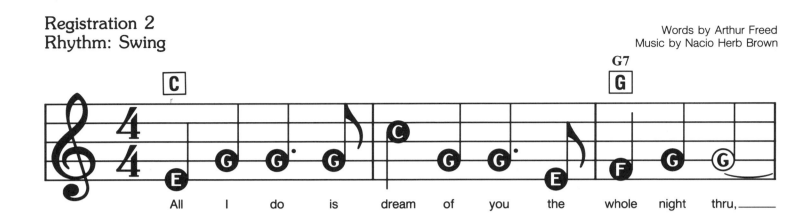

All I do is dream of you the whole night thru,

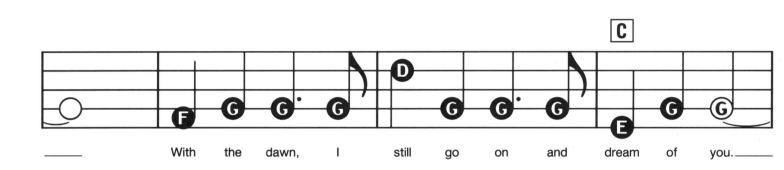

With the dawn, I still go on and dream of you.

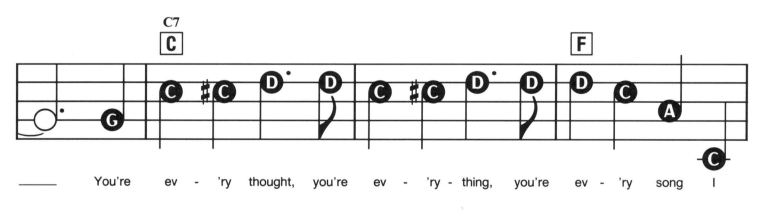

You're ev-'ry thought, you're ev-'ry-thing, you're ev-'ry song I

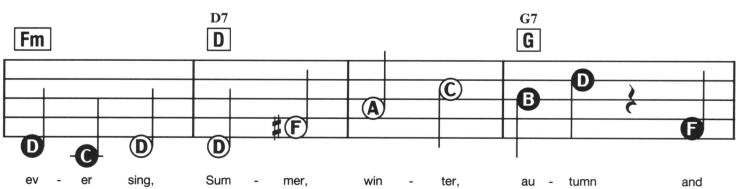

ev - er sing, Sum - mer, win - ter, au - tumn and

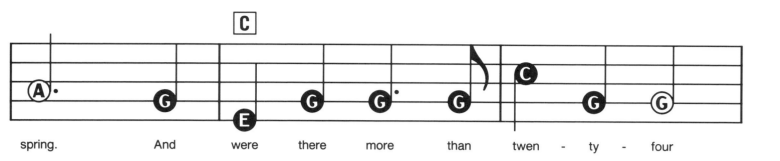

spring. And were there more than twen - ty - four

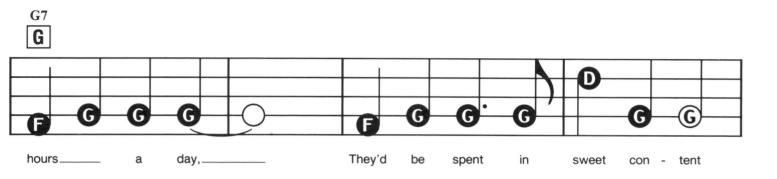

hours____ a day,____ They'd be spent in sweet con - tent

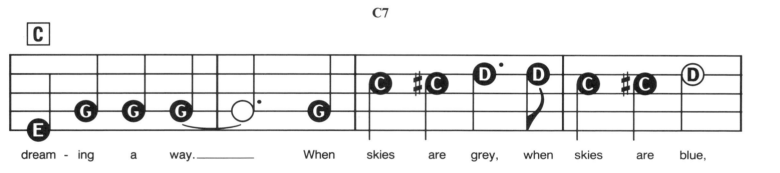

dream - ing a way.____ When skies are grey, when skies are blue,

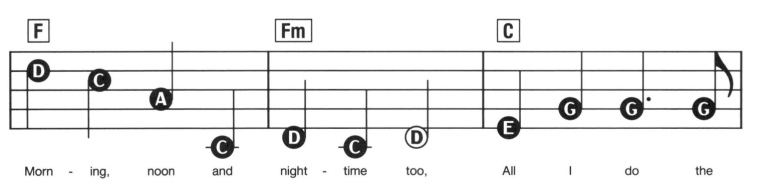

Morn - ing, noon and night - time too, All I do the

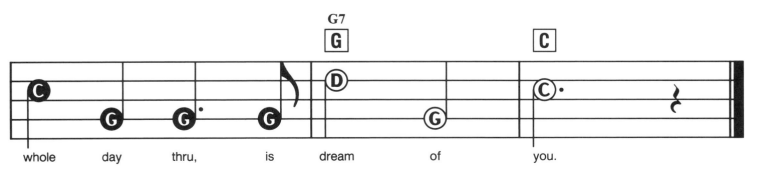

whole day thru, is dream of you.

Beyond The Blue Horizon

Registration 3
Rhythm: Fox-Trot or Rock

Words by Leo Robin
Music by Richard A. Whiting and W. Franke Harling

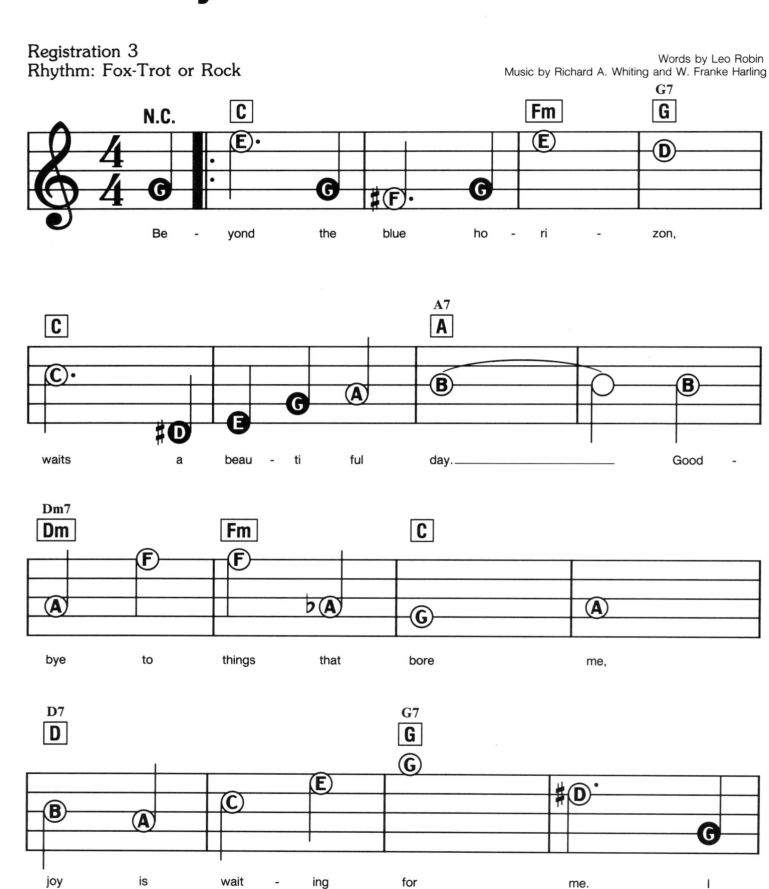

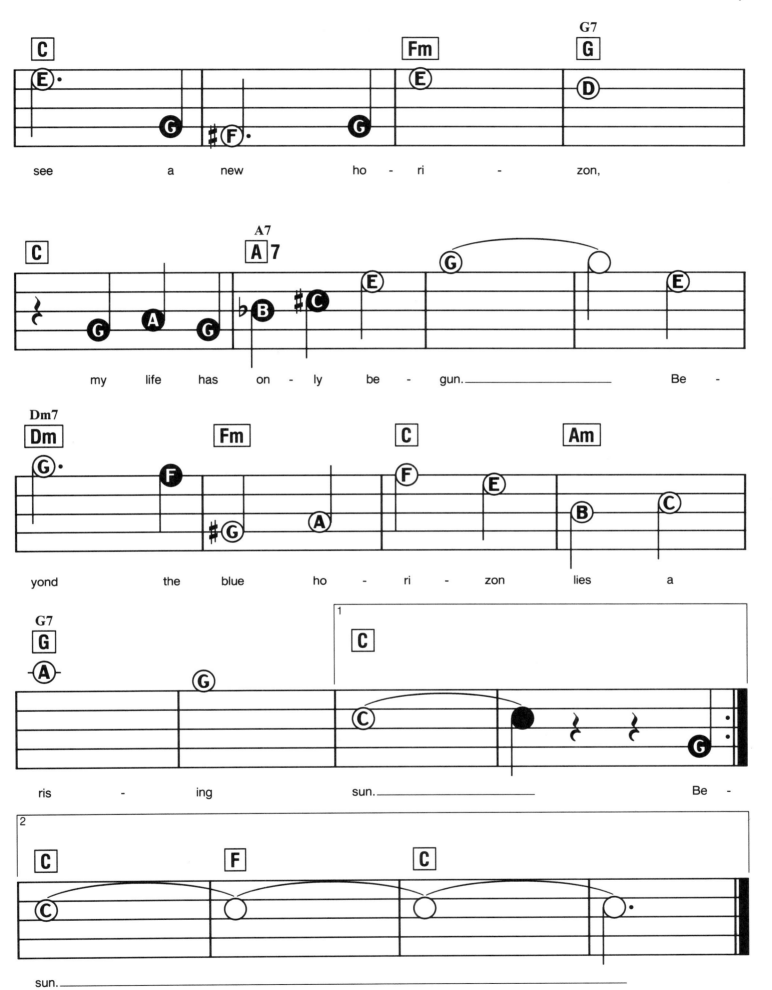

Blue Moon

Registration 8
Rhythm: Swing

Lyric by Lorenz Hart
Music by Richard Rodgers

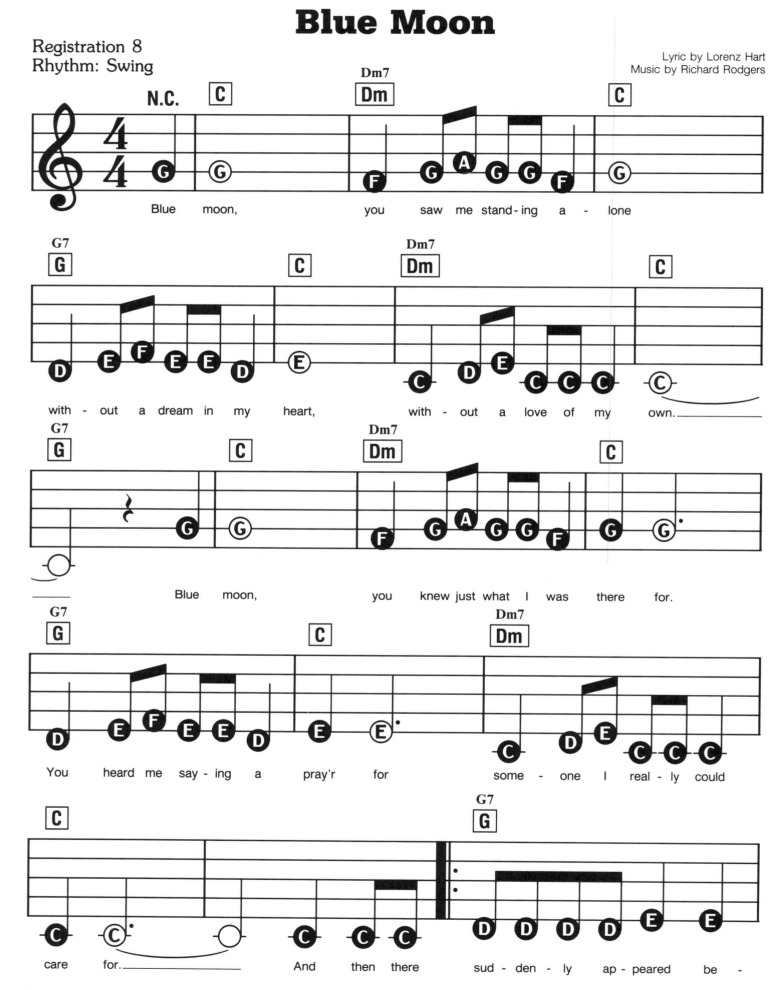

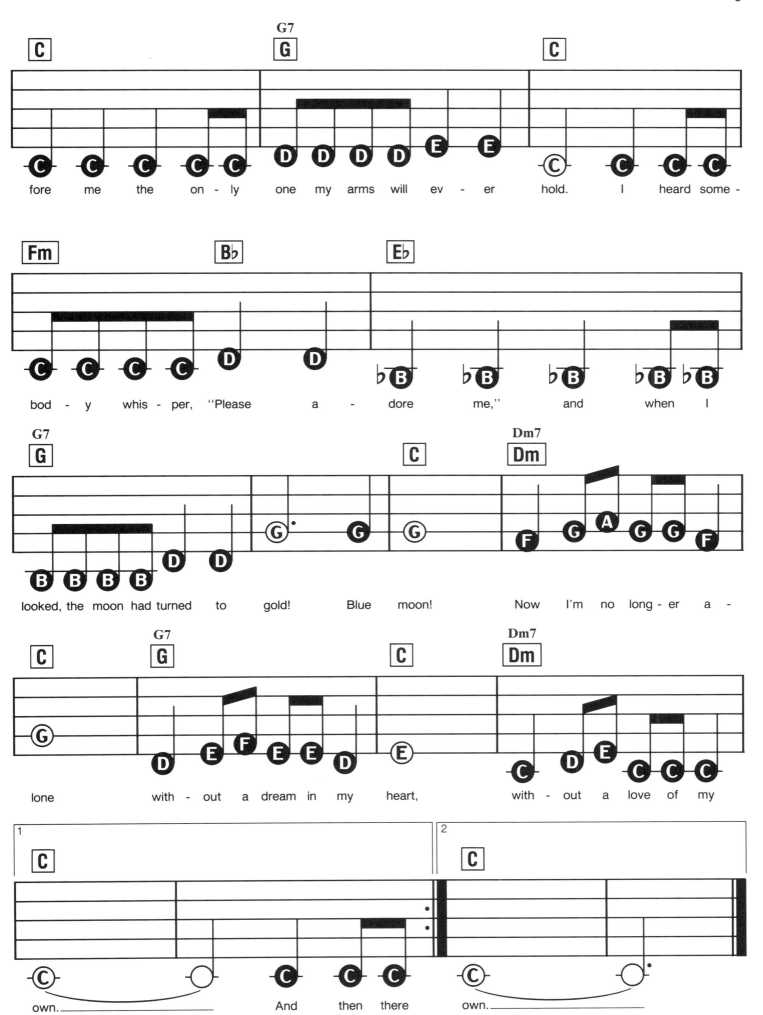

Bubbles In The Wine

Registration 8
Rhythm: Fox-Trot or Swing

Words and Music by Frank Loesser,
Bob Calame and Lawrence Welk

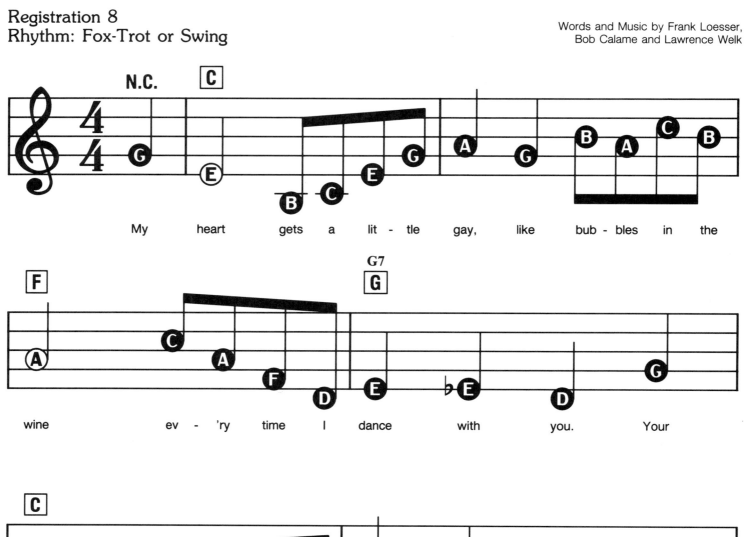

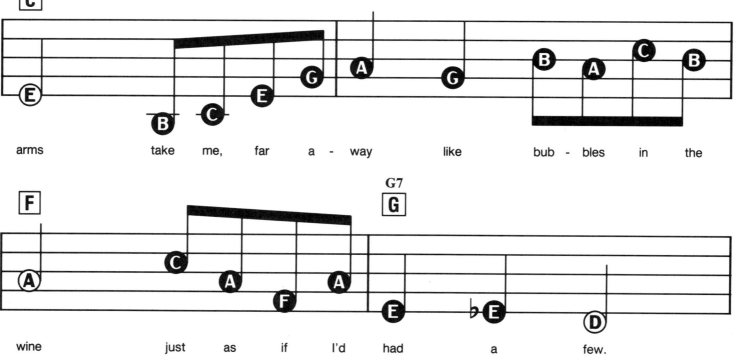

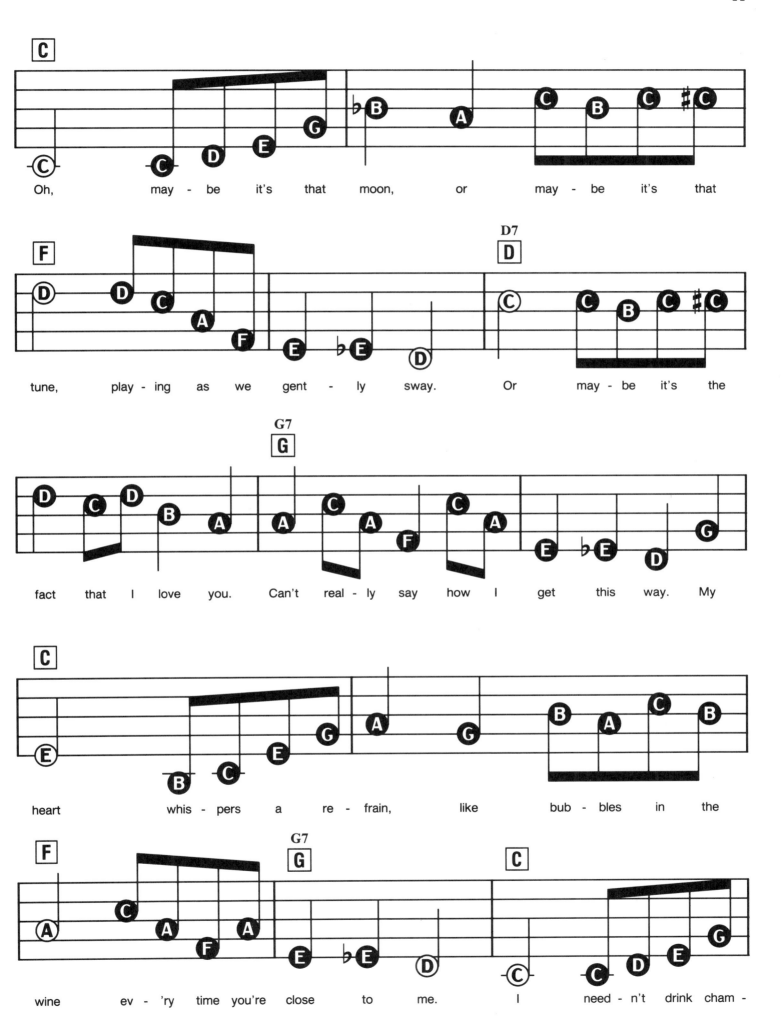

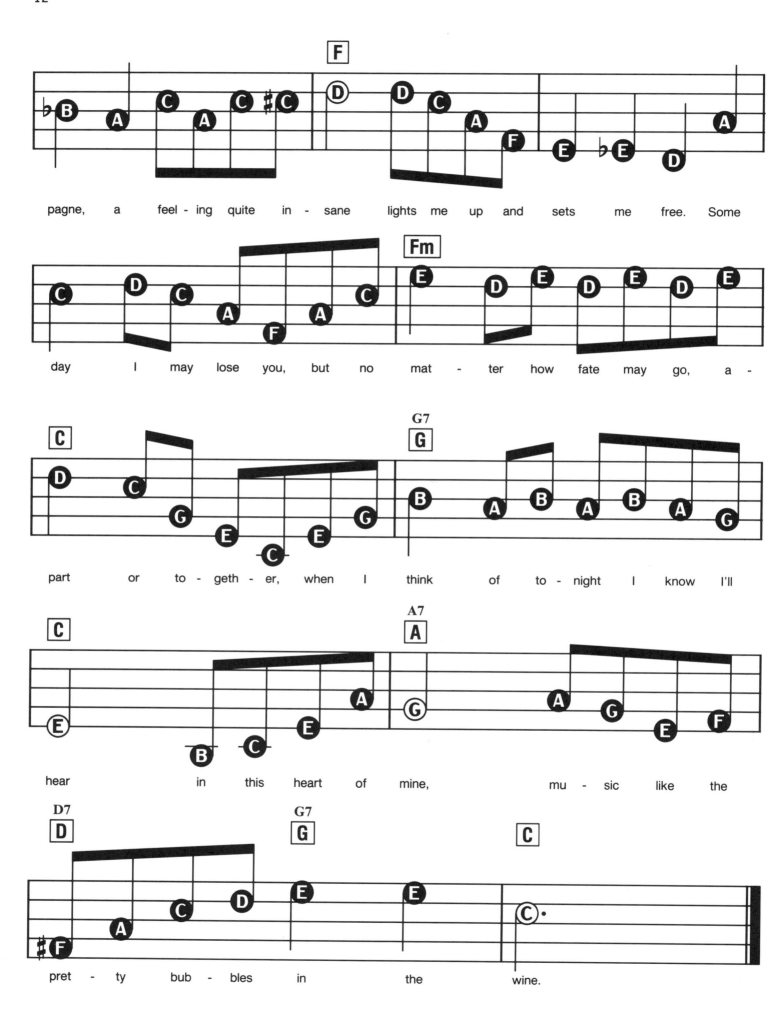

pagne, a feel-ing quite in - sane lights me up and sets me free. Some

day I may lose you, but no mat - ter how fate may go, a -

part or to-geth - er, when I think of to-night I know I'll

hear in this heart of mine, mu - sic like the

pret - ty bub - bles in the wine.

In The Cool, Cool, Cool Of The Evening

Registration 2
Rhythm: Swing

Words by Johnny Mercer
Music by Hoagy Carmichael

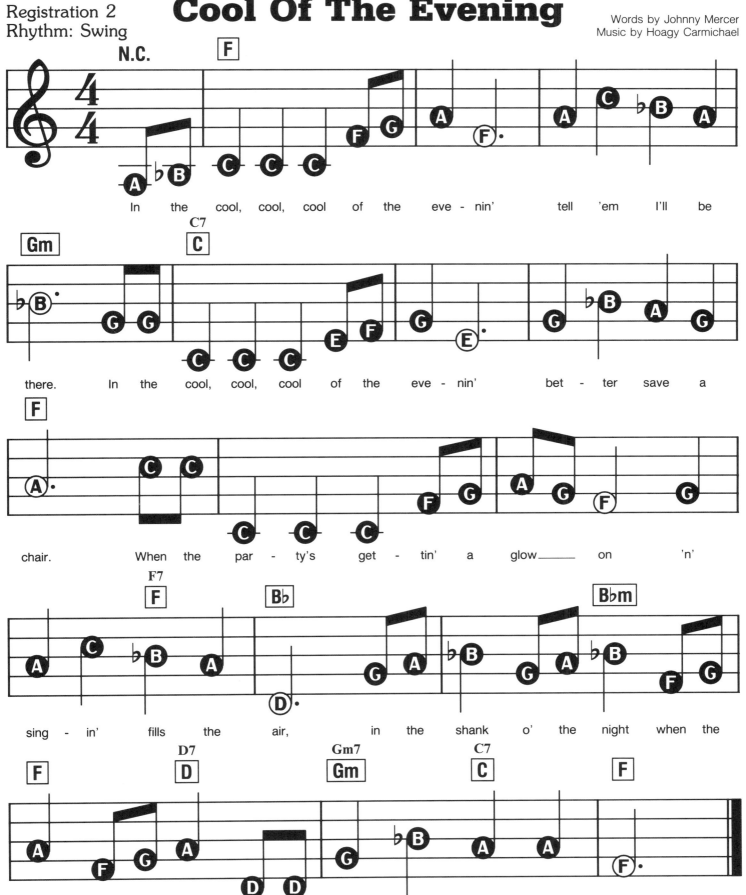

Chattanoogie Shoe Shine Boy

Registration 9
Rhythm: Swing or Big Band

Words and Music by
Harry Stone and Jack Stapp

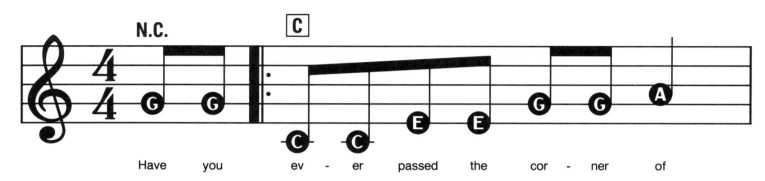

Have you ev - er passed the cor - ner of

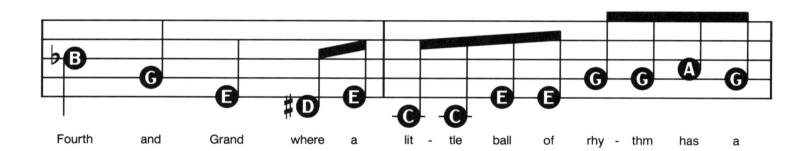

Fourth and Grand where a lit - tle ball of rhy - thm has a

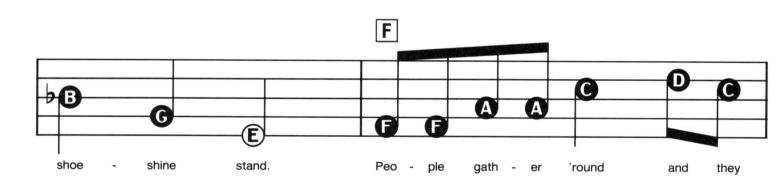

shoe - shine stand. Peo - ple gath - er 'round and they

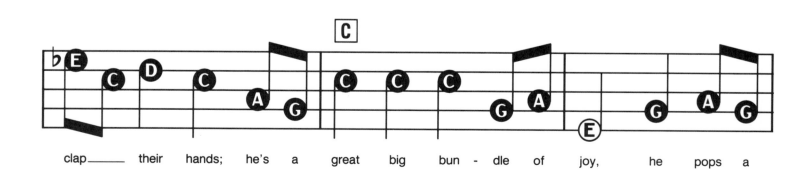

clap_____ their hands; he's a great big bun - dle of joy, he pops a

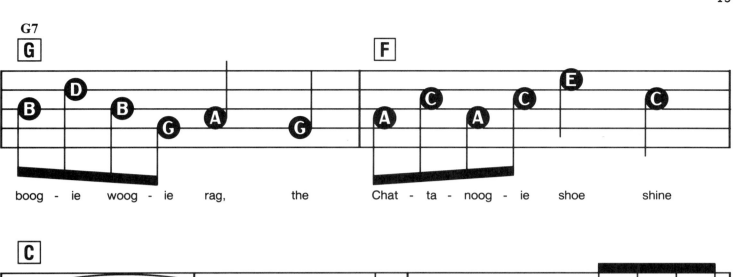

boog - ie woog - ie rag, the Chat - ta - noog - ie shoe shine

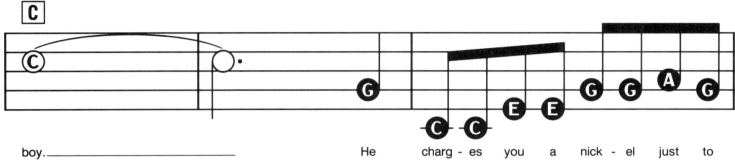

boy. He charg - es you a nick - el just to

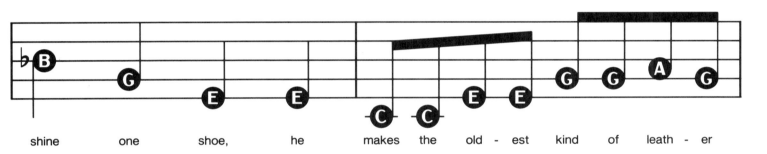

shine one shoe, he makes the old - est kind of leath - er

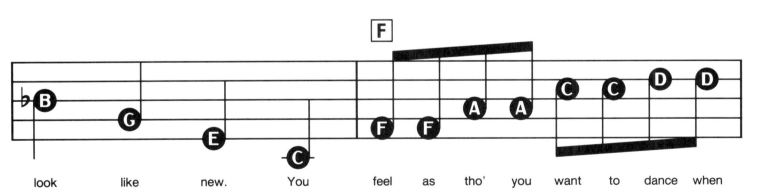

look like new. You feel as tho' you want to dance when

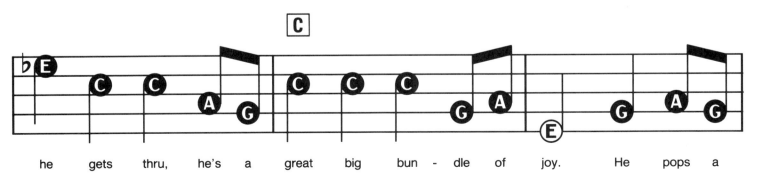

he gets thru, he's a great big bun - dle of joy. He pops a

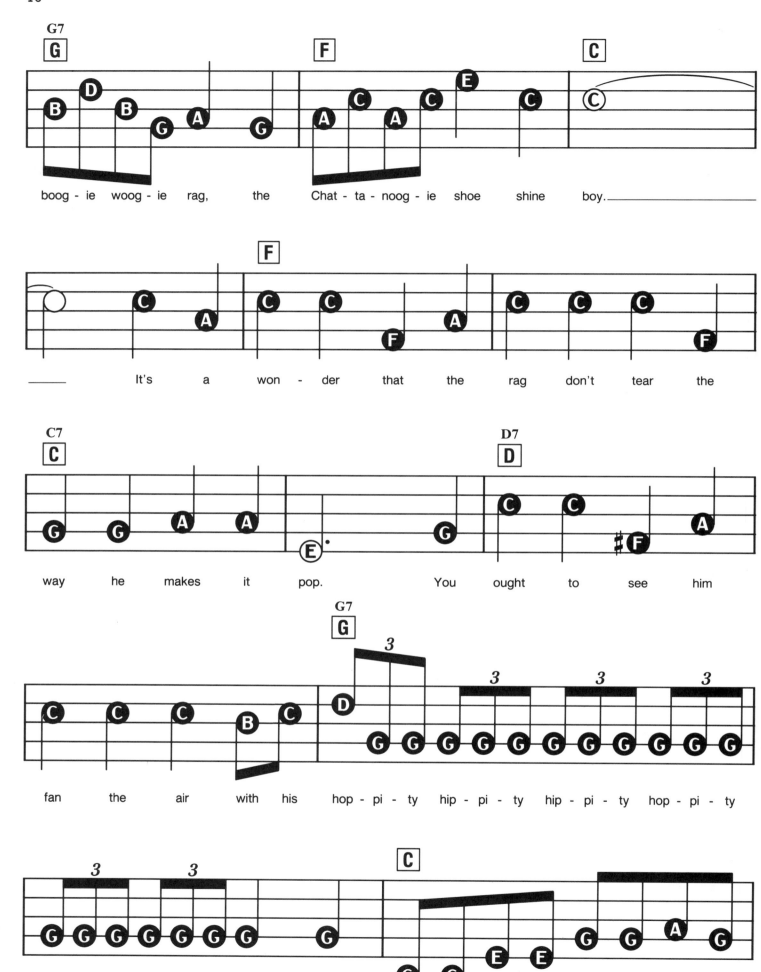

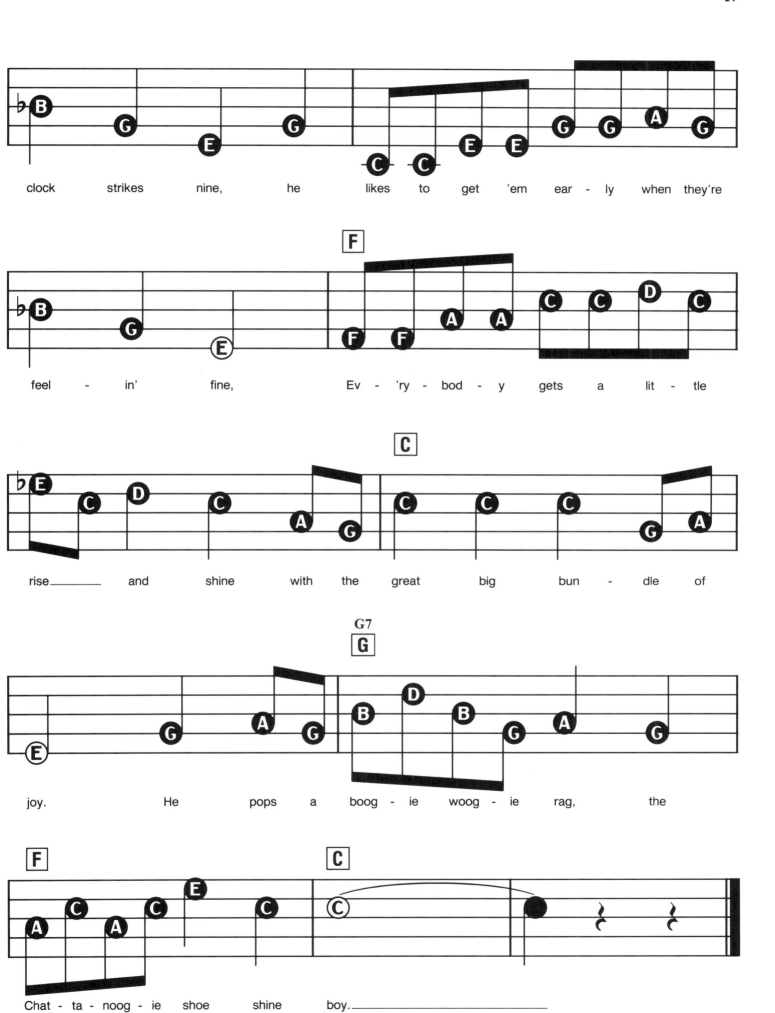

The Darktown Strutters' Ball

Registration 8
Rhythm: Polka, Fox-Trot, or Dixie

Words and Music by
Shelton Brooks

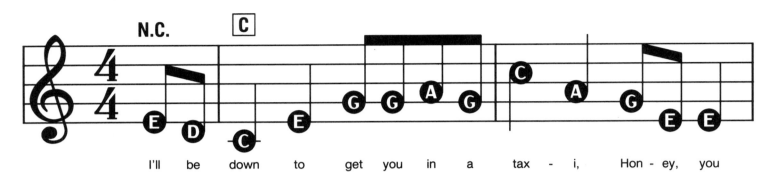

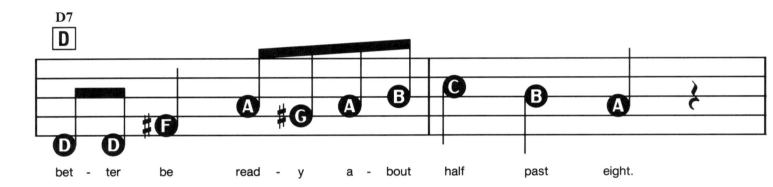

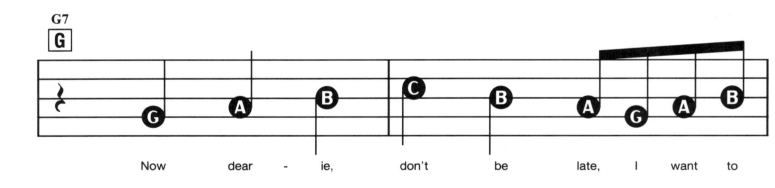

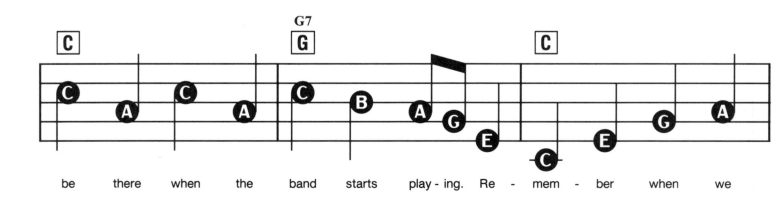

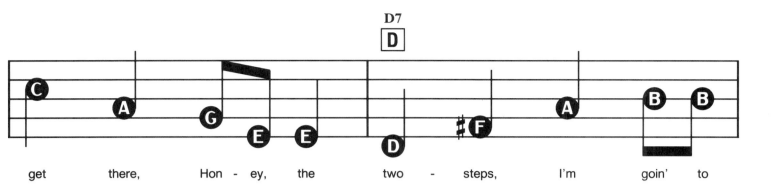

get there, Hon - ey, the two - steps, I'm goin' to

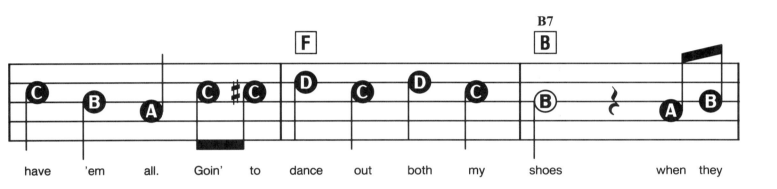

have 'em all. Goin' to dance out both my shoes when they

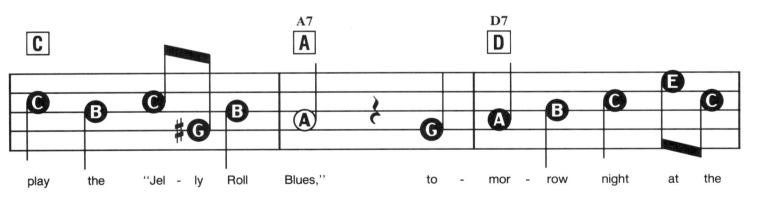

play the "Jel - ly Roll Blues," to - mor - row night at the

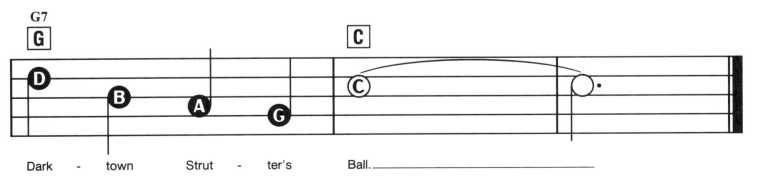

Dark - town Strut - ter's Ball.

Diane

Registration 10
Rhythm: Waltz

Words and Music by
Erno Rapee and Lew Pollack

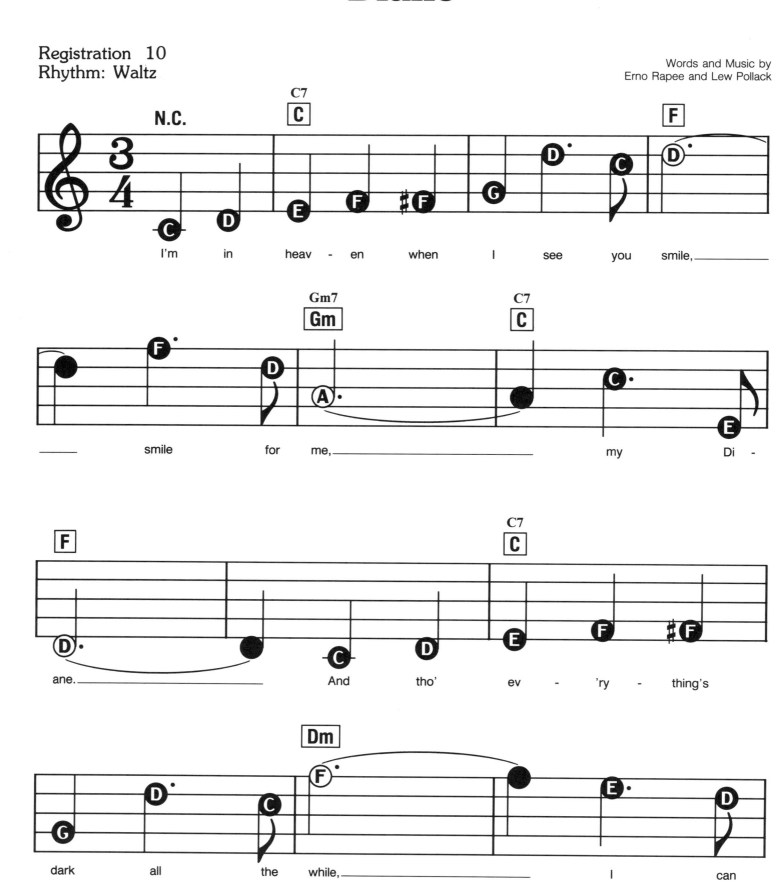

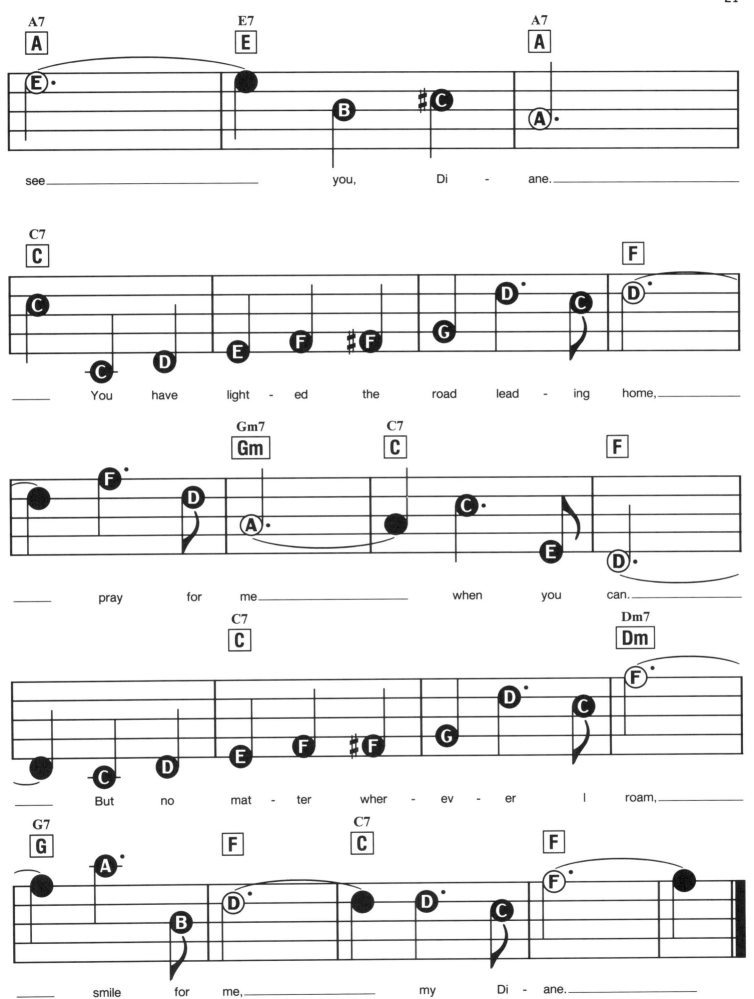

Does Your Heart Beat For Me?

Registration 3
Rhythm: Swing

Words by Mitchell Parish
Music by Russ Morgan and Arnold Johnson

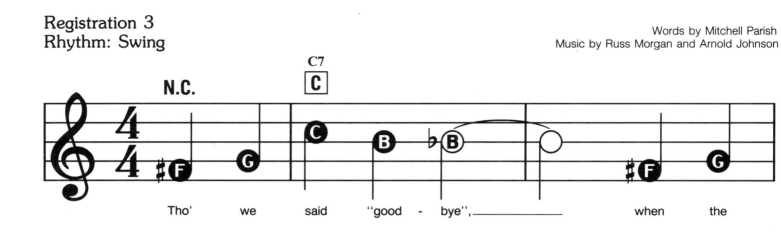

Tho' we said "good - bye", _____ when the

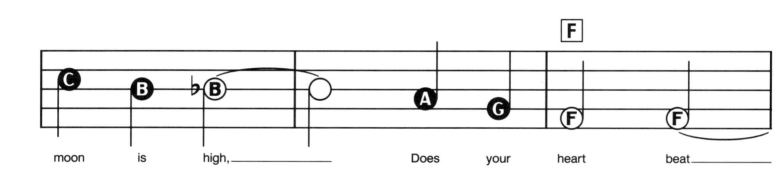

moon is high, _____ Does your heart beat _____

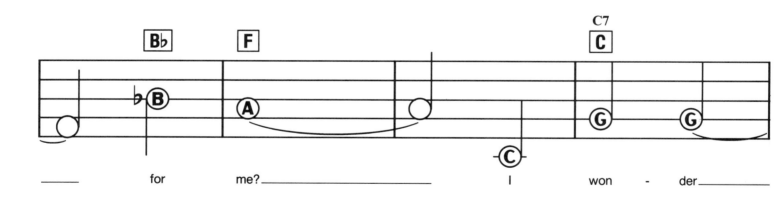

_____ for me? _____ I won - der _____

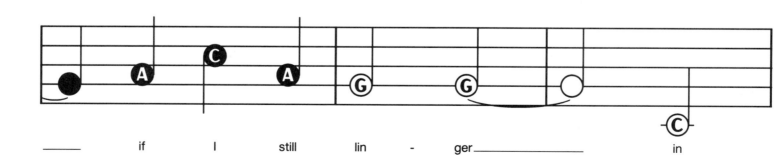

_____ if I still lin - ger _____ in

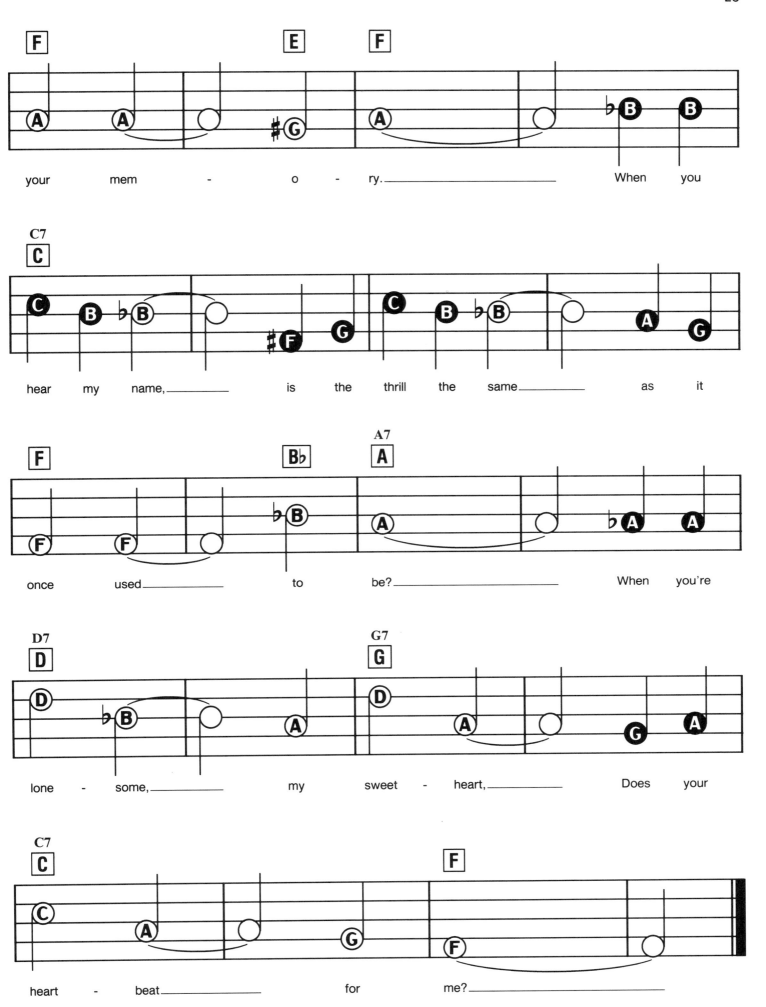

Don't Sit Under The Apple Tree
(With Anyone Else But Me)

Registration 2
Rhythm: Polka or Fox-Trot

Words and Music by Lew Brown,
Charlie Tobias and Sam H. Stept

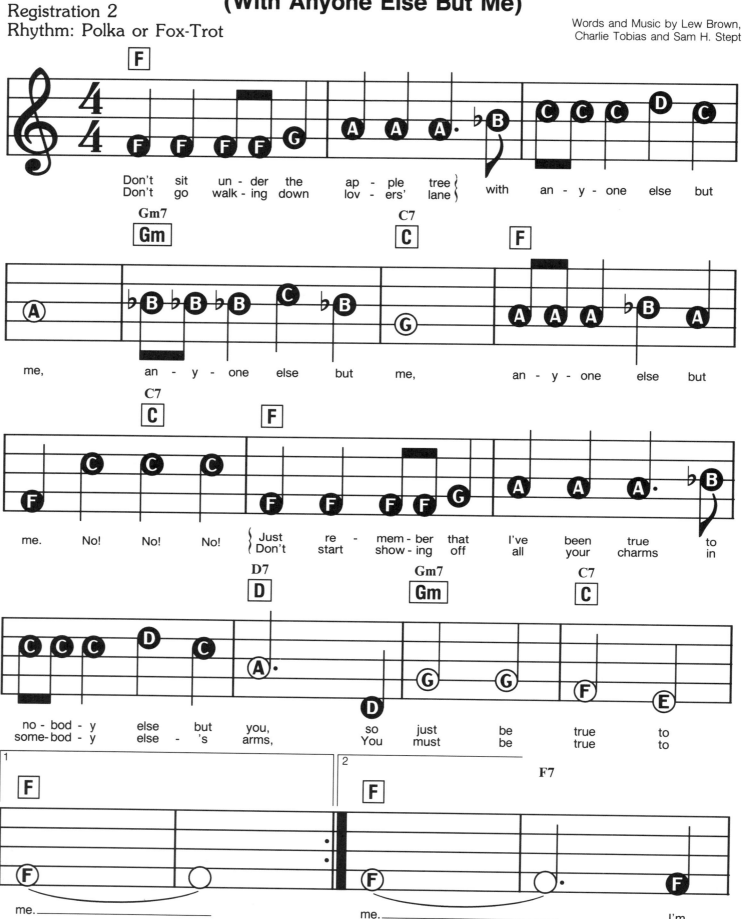

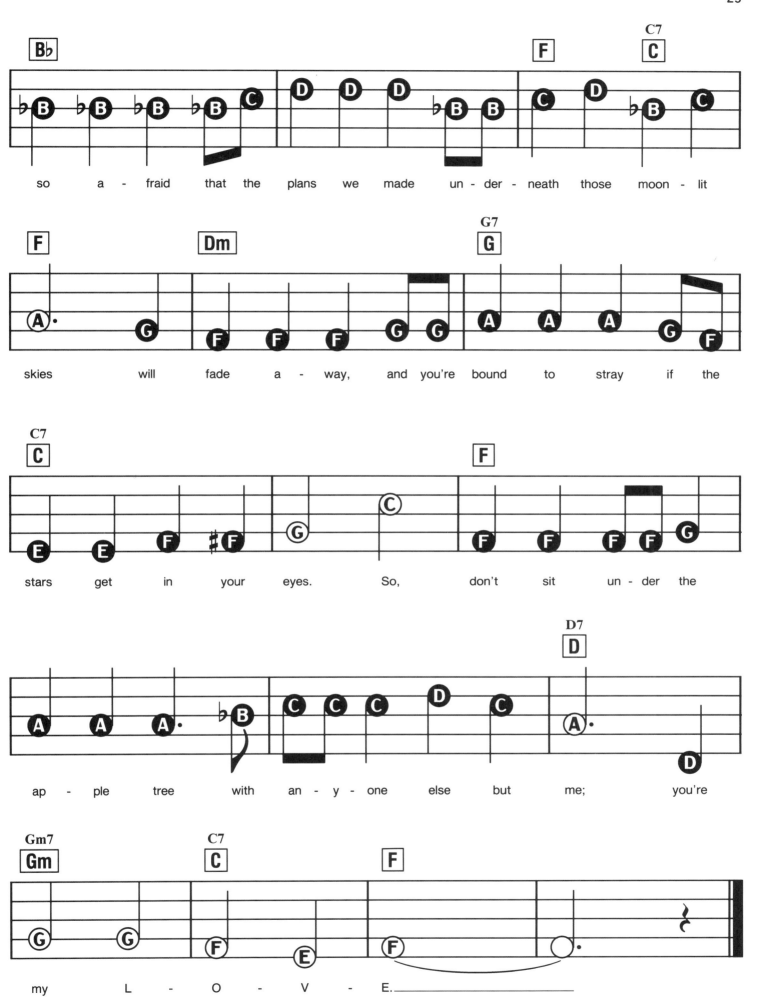

Elmer's Tune

Registration 1
Rhythm: Swing or Shuffle

Words and Music by Elmer Albrecht,
Sammy Gallop and Dick Jurgens

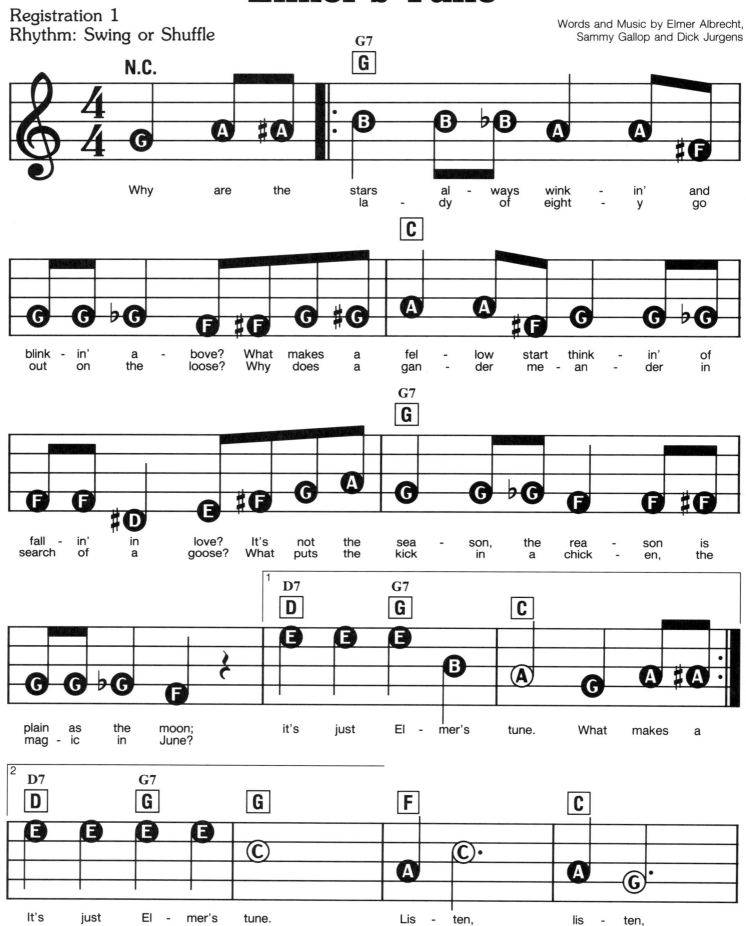

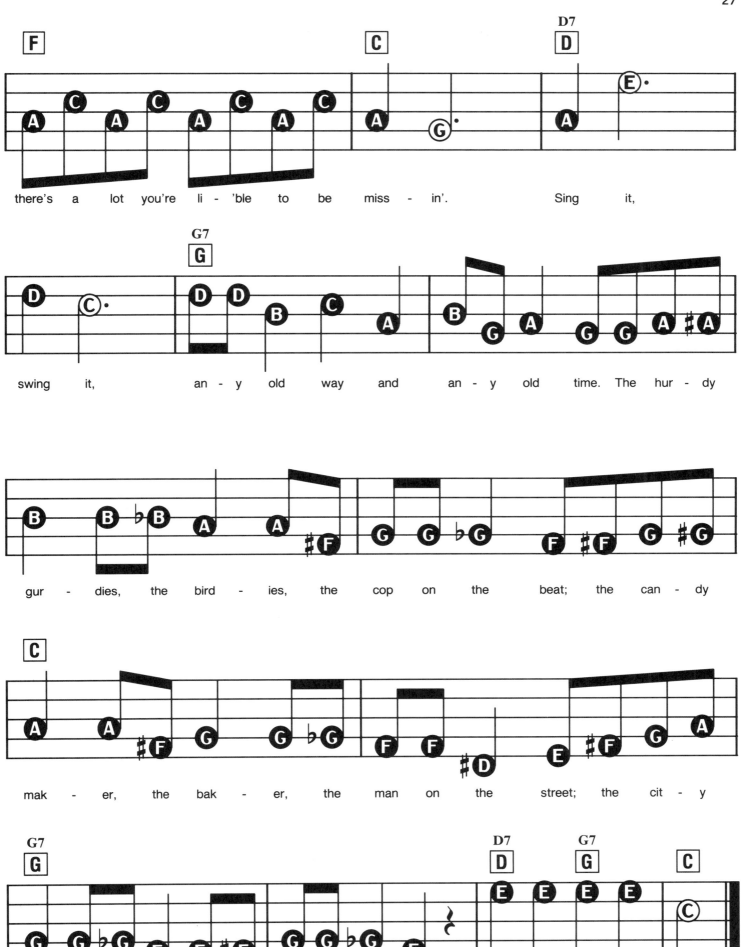

Emily

Registration 3
Rhythm: Waltz

Lyric by Johnny Mercer
Music by Johnny Mandel

29

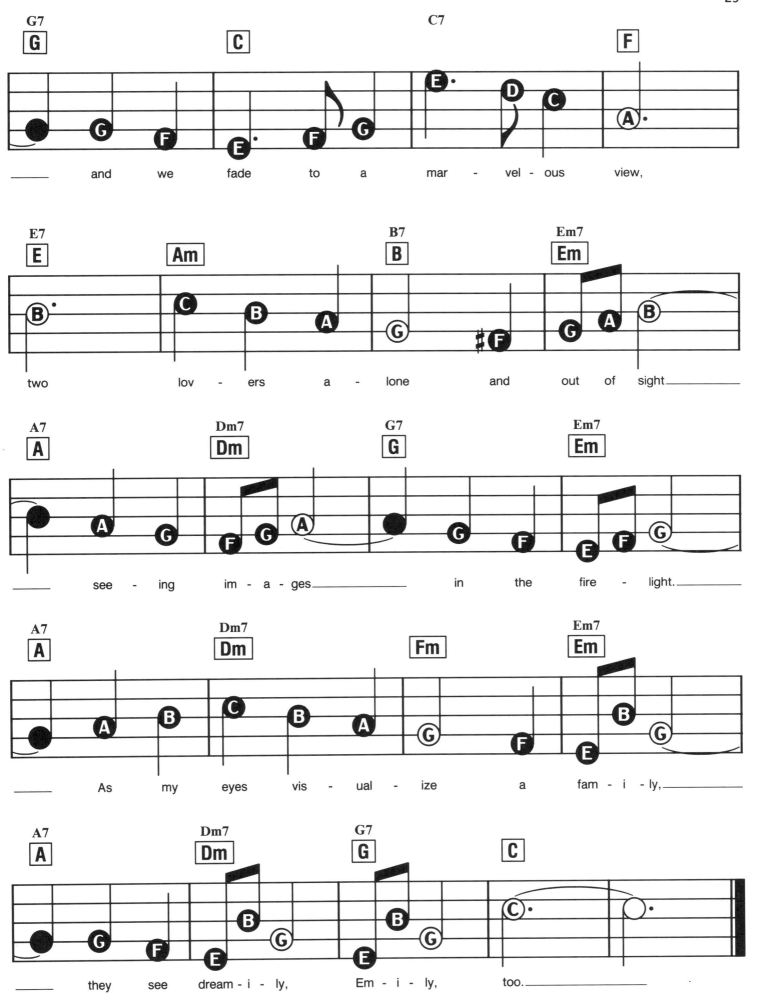

Everything I Have Is Yours

Registration 4
Rhythm: Swing or Fox-Trot

Words by Harold Adamson
Music by Burton Lane

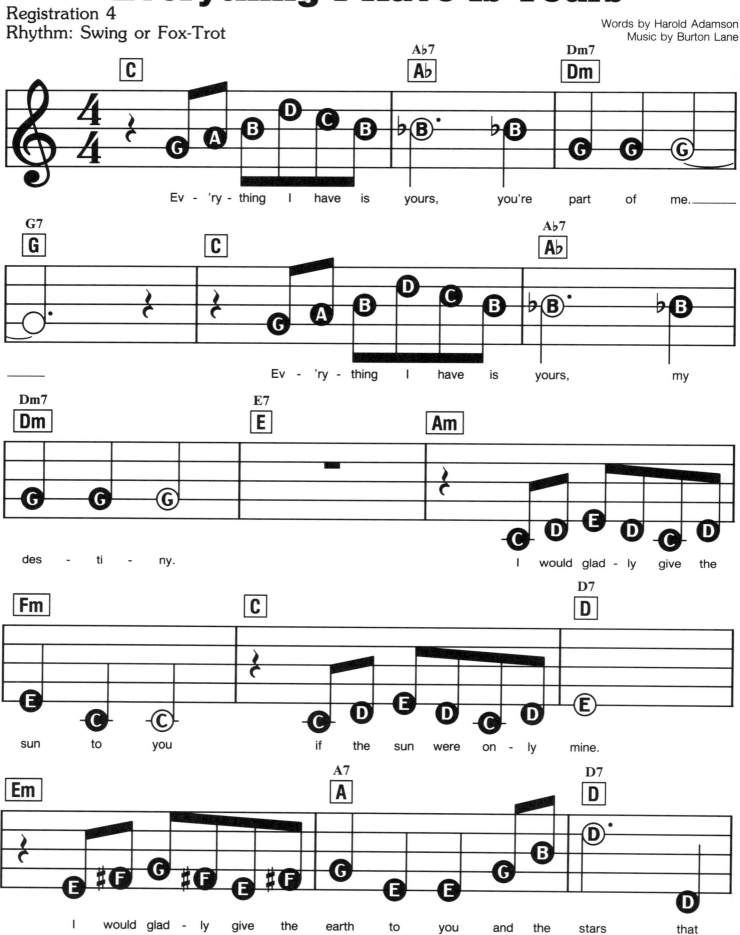

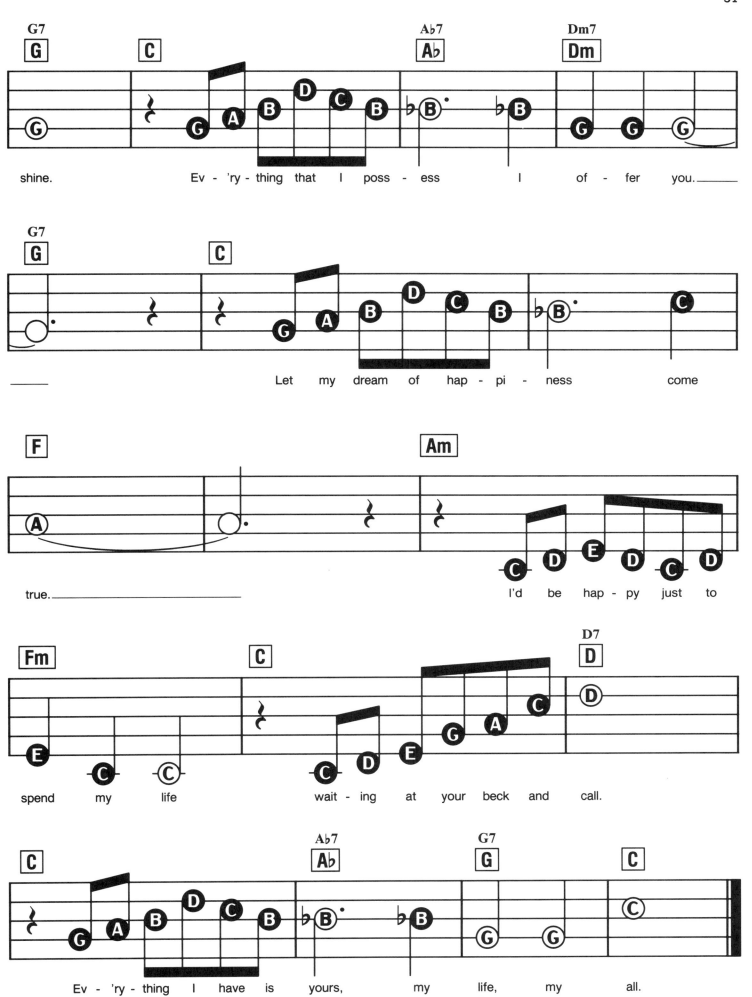

Goodbye, My Coney Island Baby

Registration 5
Rhythm: Fox-Trot or Swing

Words and Music by
Les Applegate

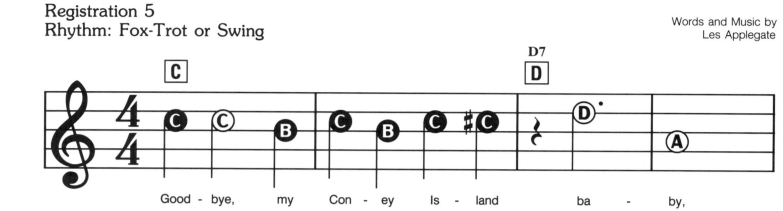

Good - bye, my Con - ey Is - land ba - by,

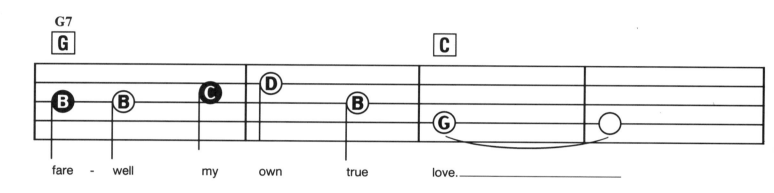

fare - well my own true love._____

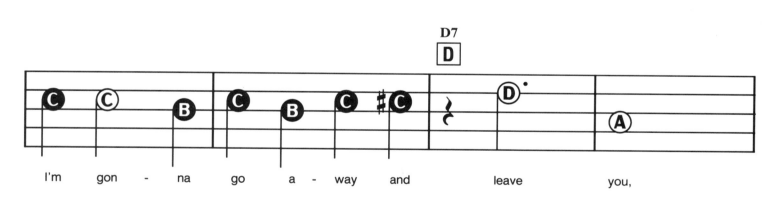

I'm gon - na go a - way and leave you,

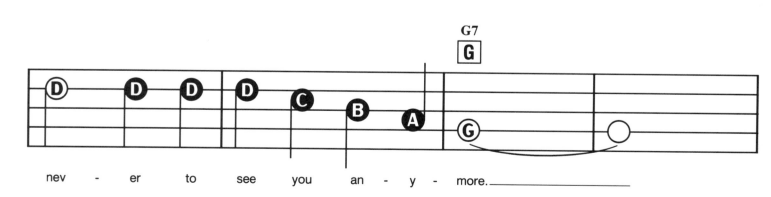

nev - er to see you an - y - more._____

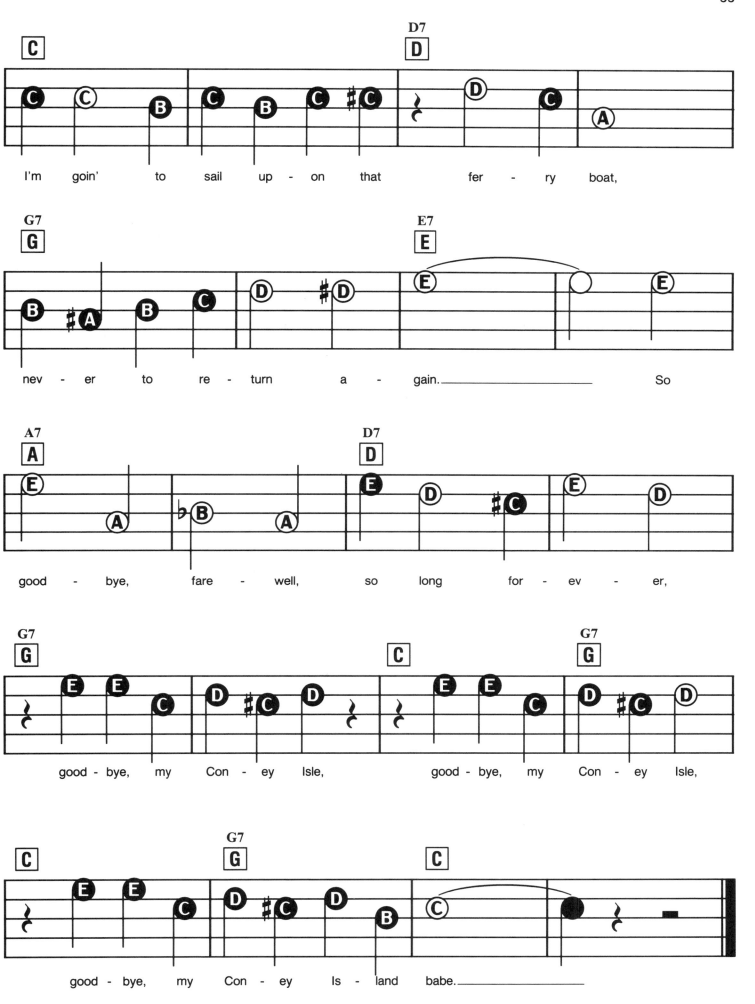

The Green Leaves Of Summer

Registration 3
Rhythm: Waltz

Words by Paul Francis Webster
Music by Dimitri Tiomkin

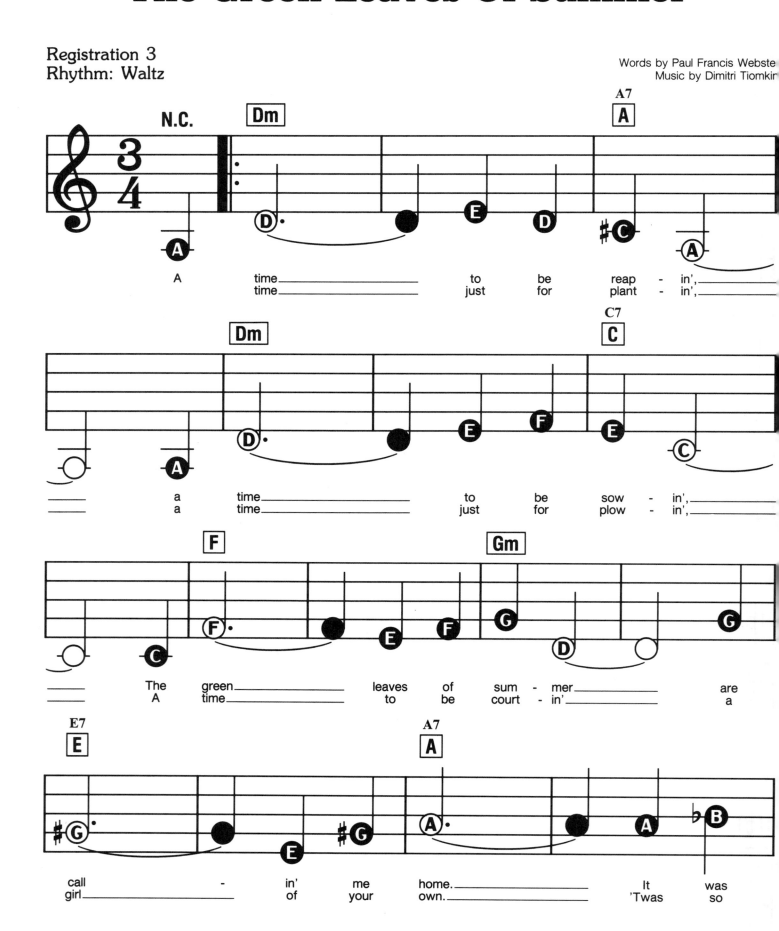

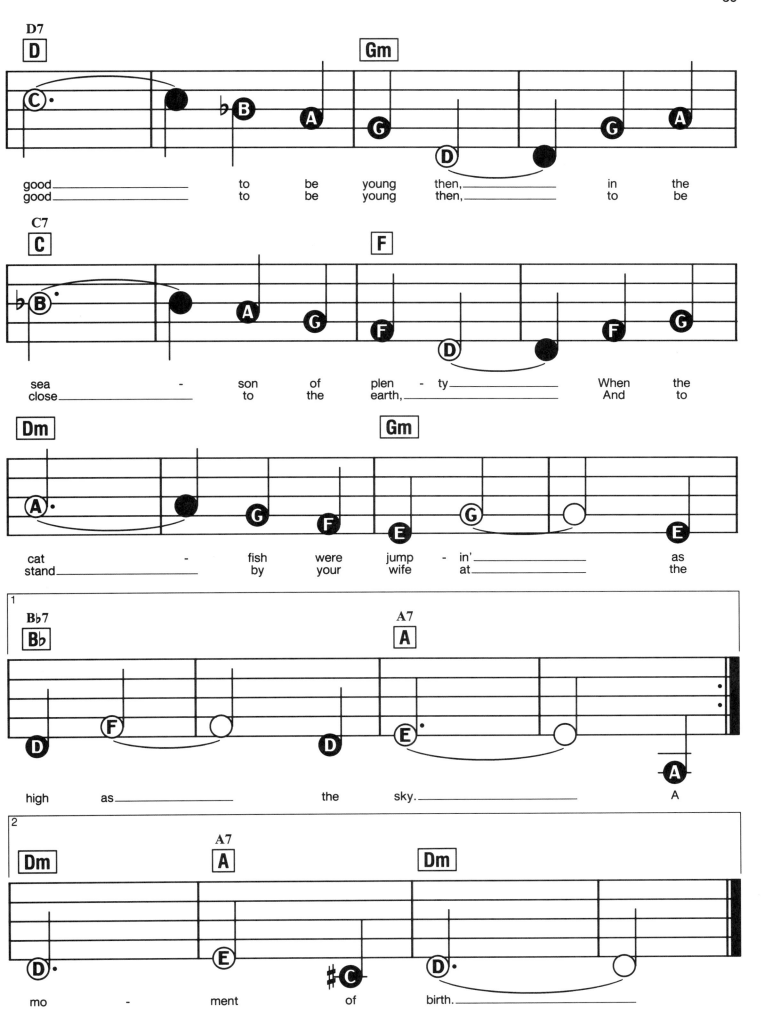

Hey, Look Me Over

(From "WILDCAT")

Registration 3
Rhythm: ⁶⁄₈ March

Lyric by Carolyn Leigh
Music by Cy Coleman

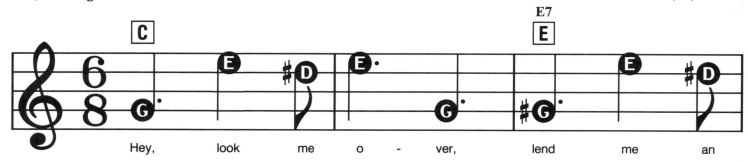

Hey, look me o - ver, lend me an

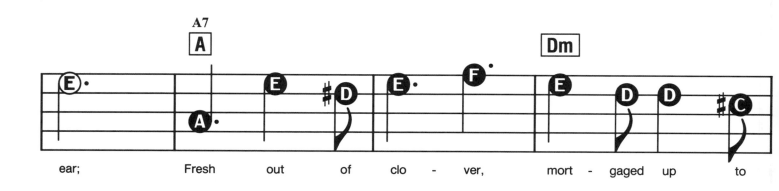

ear; Fresh out of clo - ver, mort - gaged up to

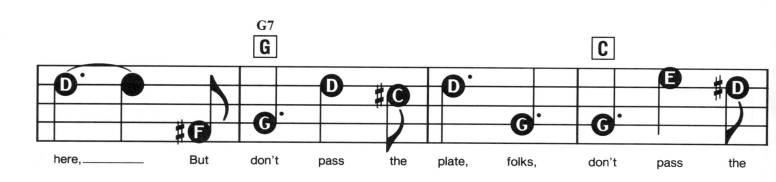

here, _____ But don't pass the plate, folks, don't pass the

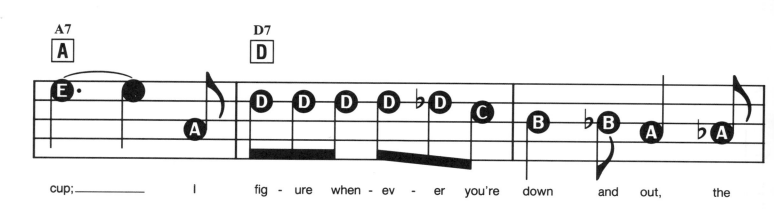

cup; _____ I fig - ure when - ev - er you're down and out, the

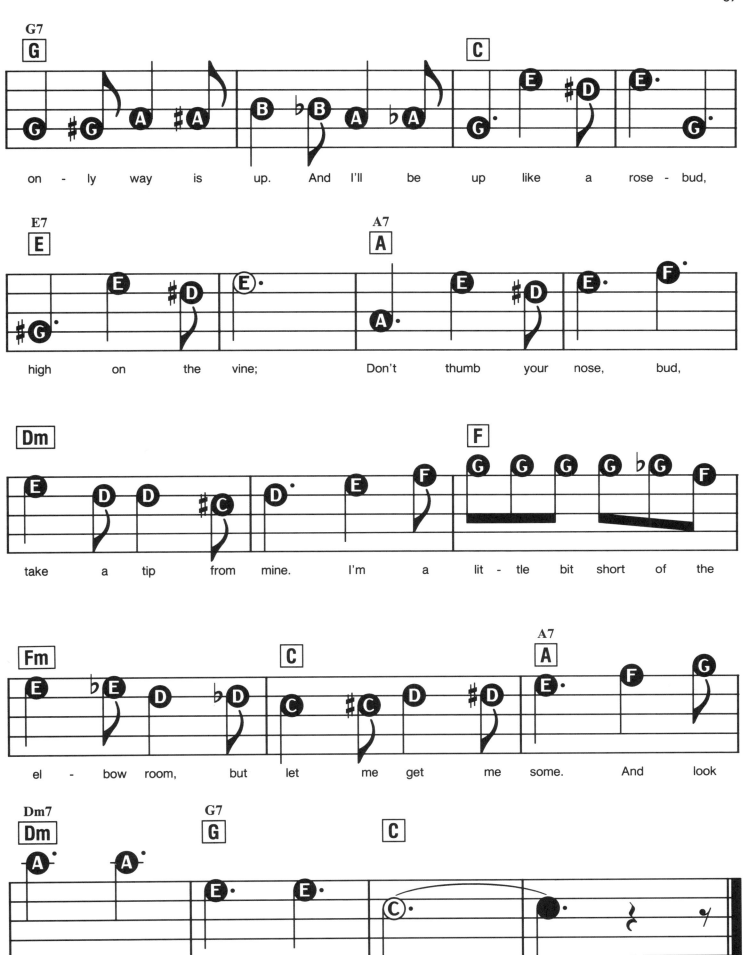

I Cried For You

Registration 9
Rhythm: Swing or Jazz

Words and Music by Arthur Freed,
Gus Arnheim and Abe Lyman

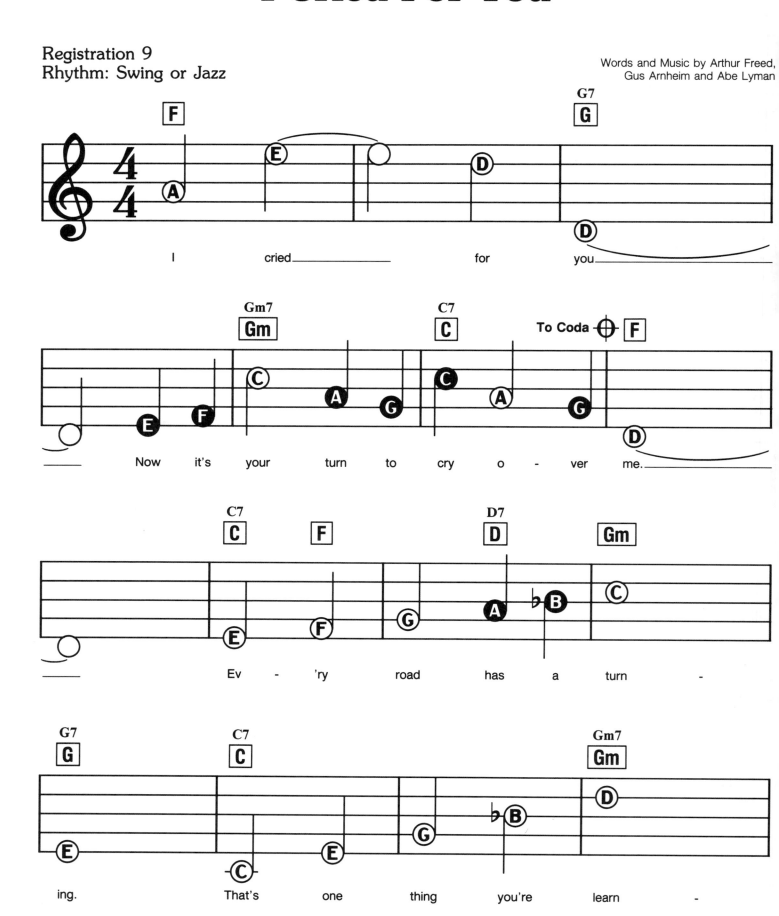

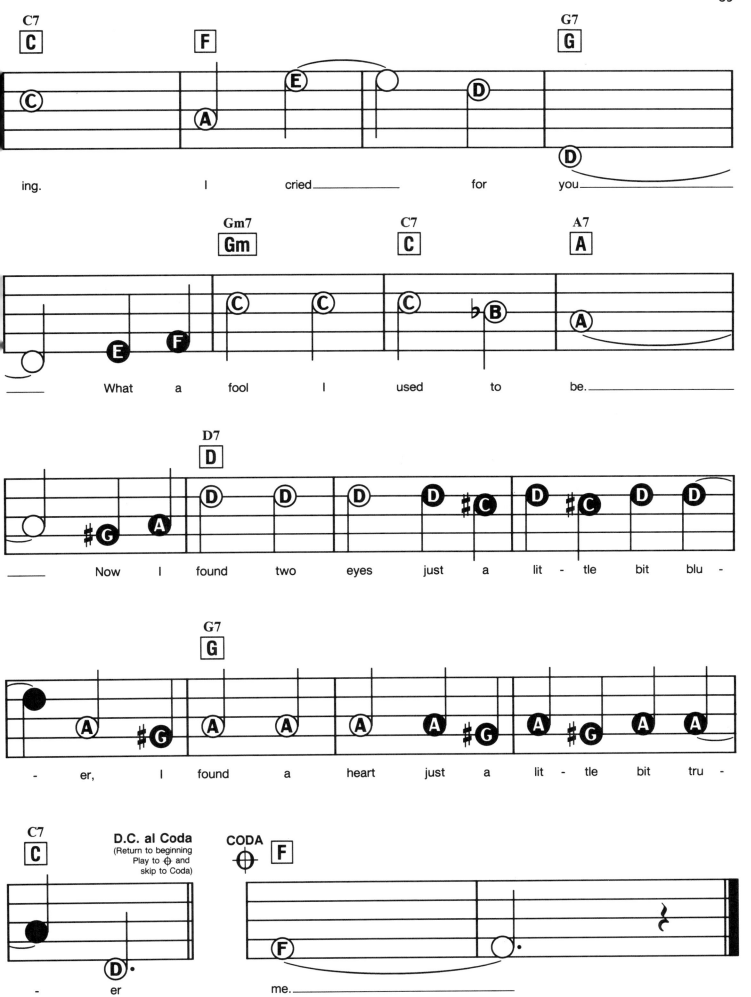

I'm Getting Sentimental Over You

Registration 1
Rhythm: Swing

Words by Ned Washington
Music by George Bassman

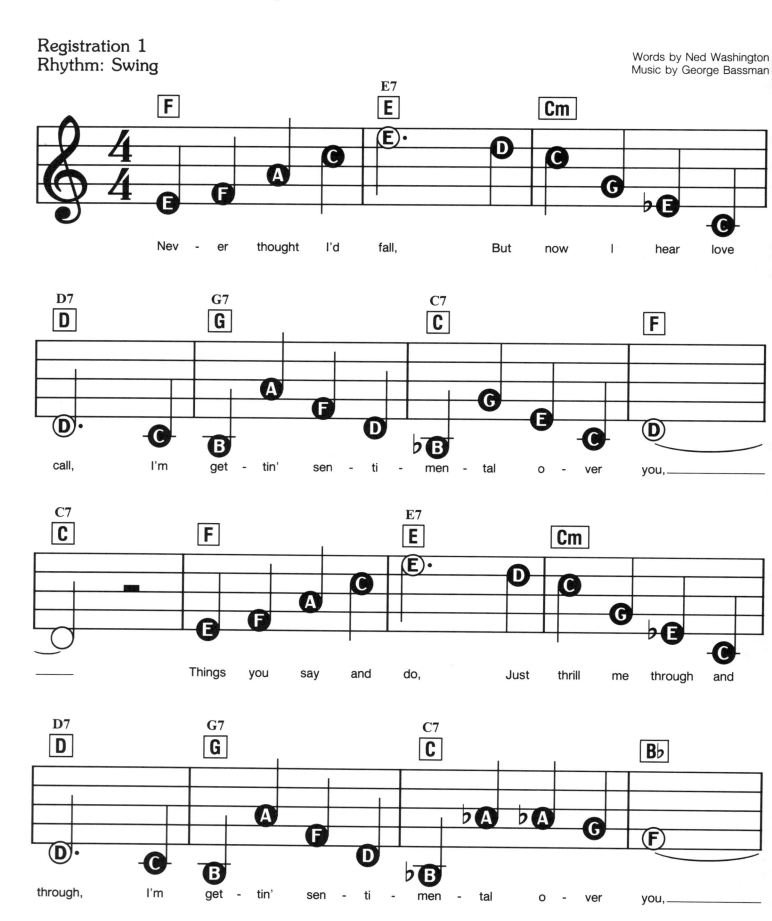

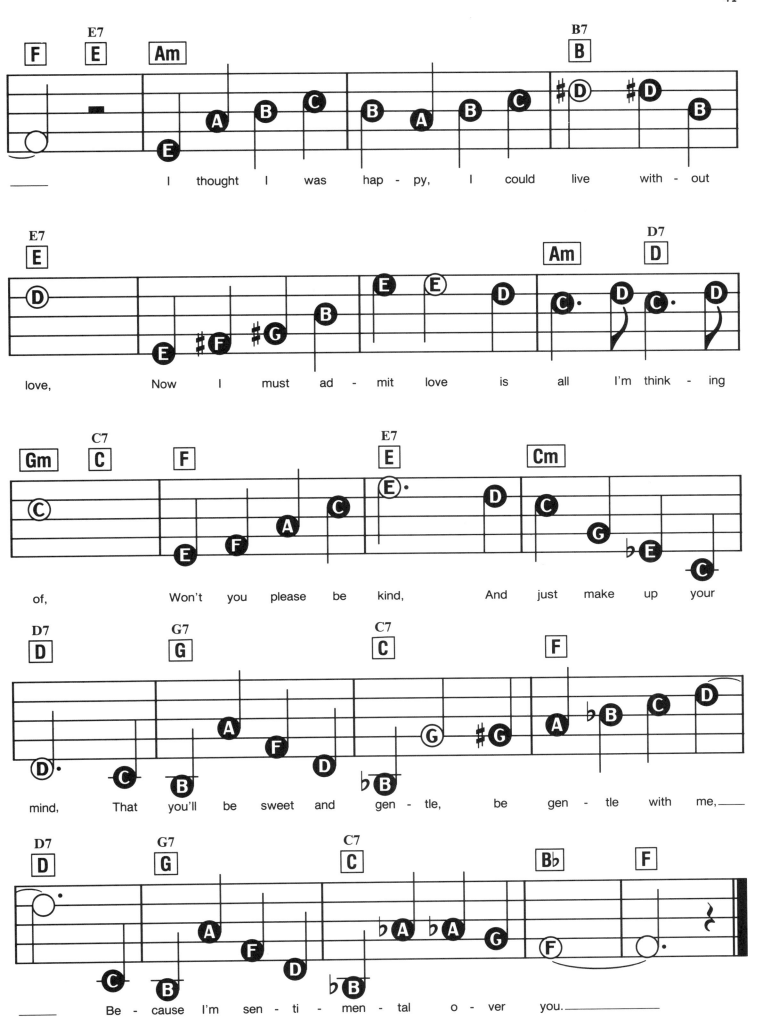

Isn't It Romantic

Registration 2
Rhythm: Swing or Big Band

Lyric by Lorenz Hart
Music by Richard Rodgers

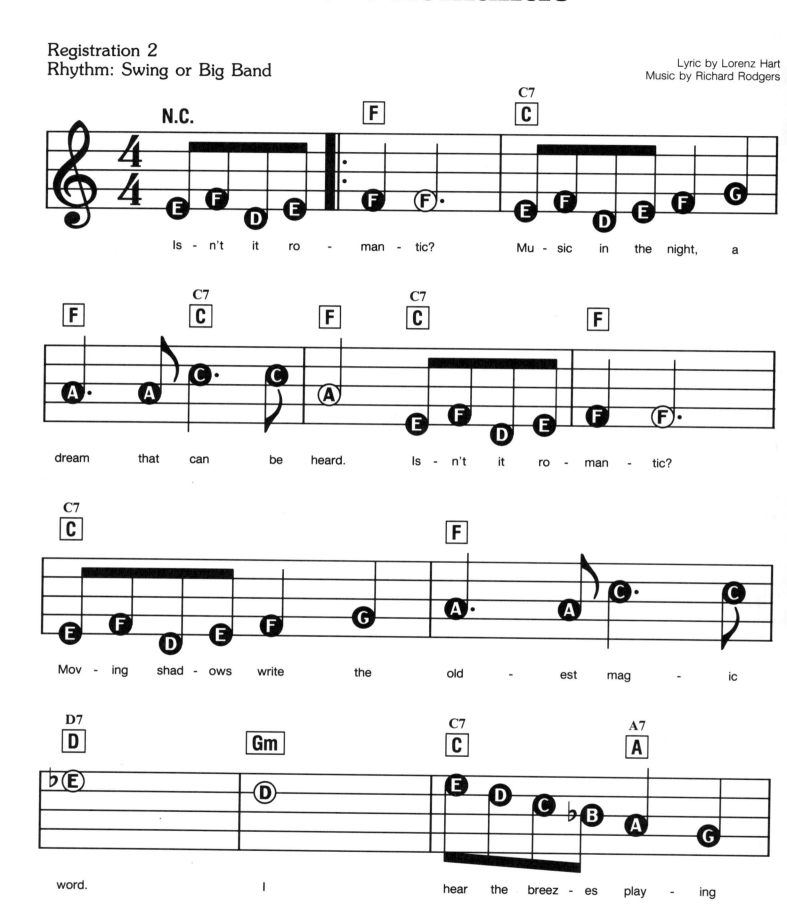

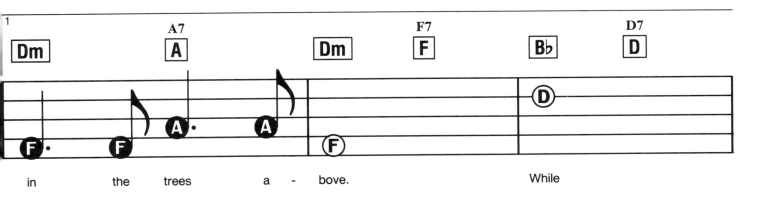

in the trees a - bove. While

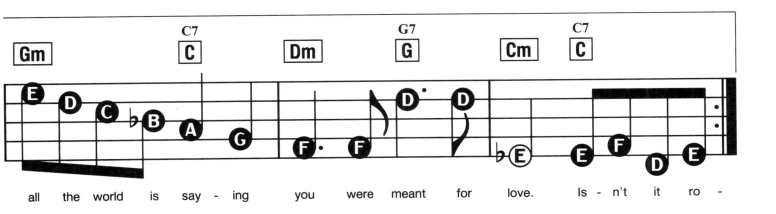

all the world is say - ing you were meant for love. Is - n't it ro -

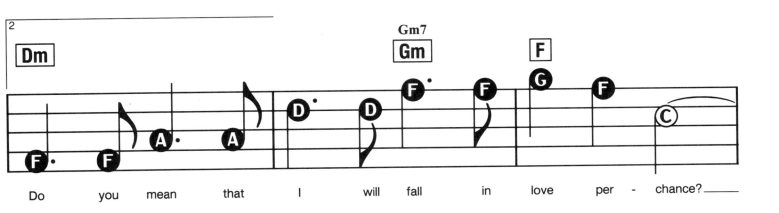

Do you mean that I will fall in love per - chance?

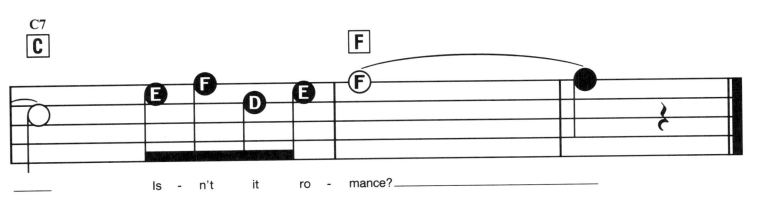

Is - n't it ro - mance?

It Don't Mean A Thing
(If It Ain't Got That Swing)

Registration 7
Rhythm: Swing

Words by Irving Mills
Music by Duke Ellington

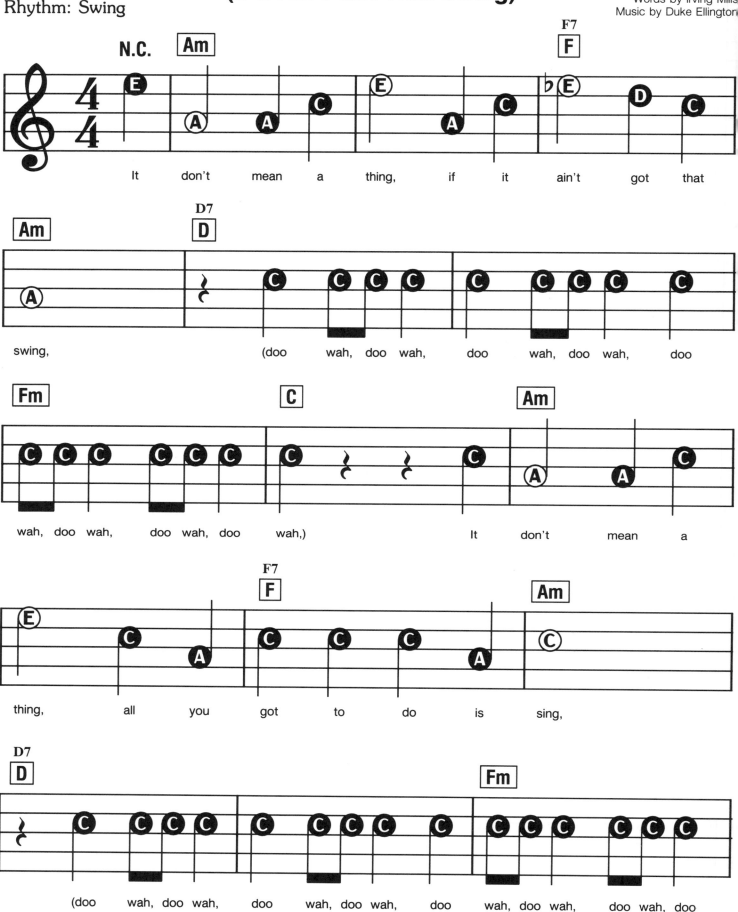

45

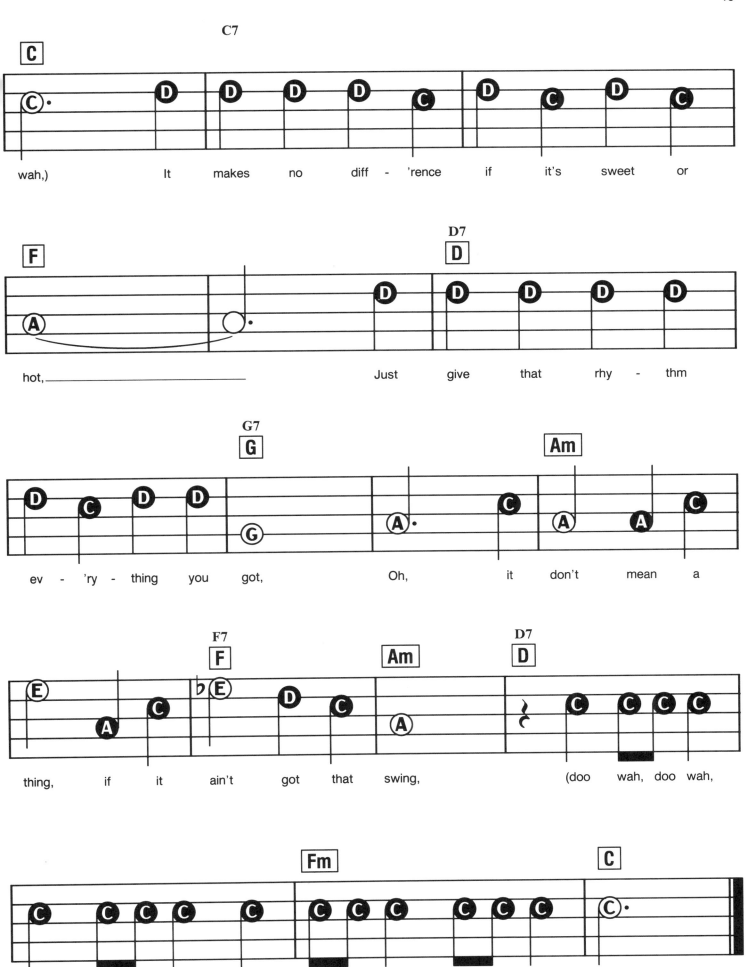

Ja-Da

Registration 2
Rhythm: Fox-Trot, Swing, or Shuffle

Words and Music by Bob Carleton
Revised Lyric and Arrangement by
Nan Wynn and Ken Lane

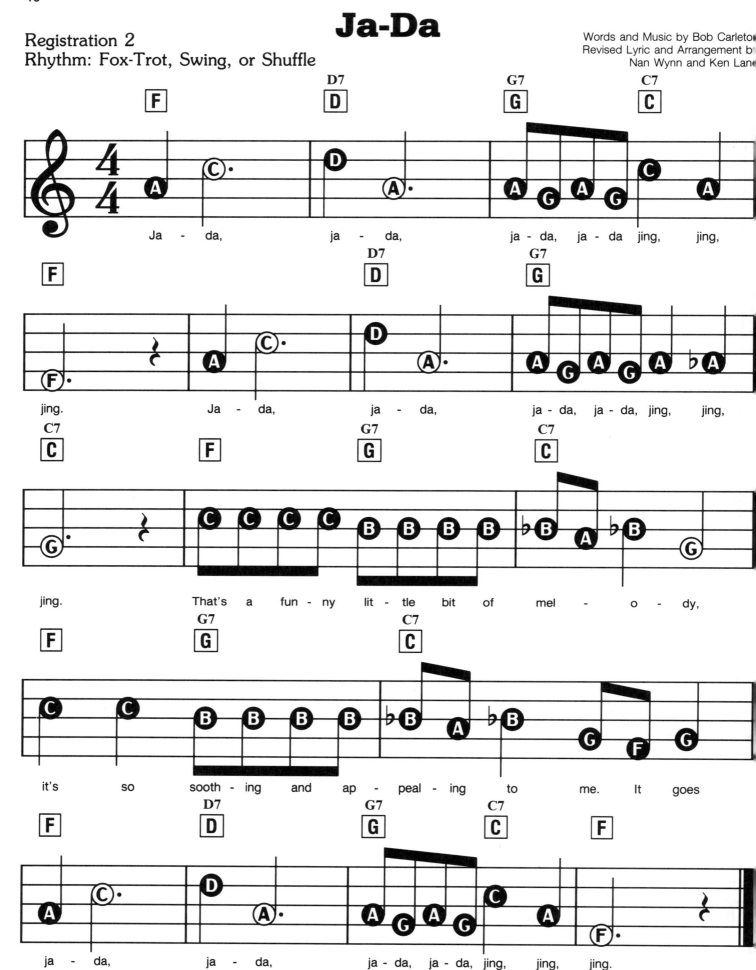

One Morning In May

Registration 1
Rhythm: Fox-Trot or Swing

Words by Mitchell Parish
Music by Hoagy Carmichael

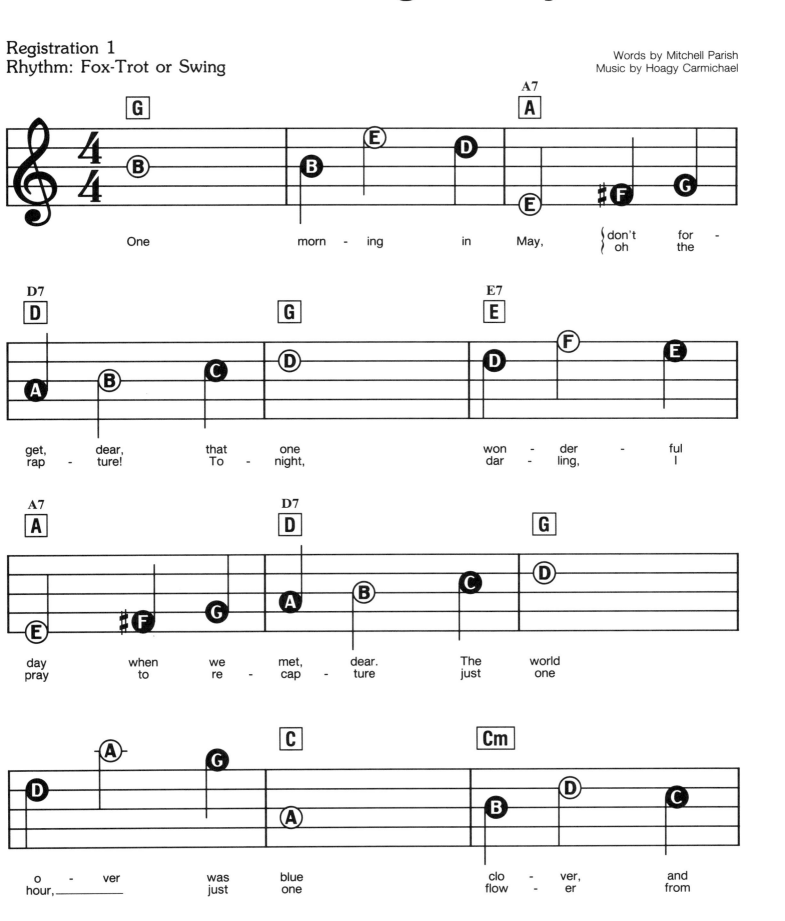

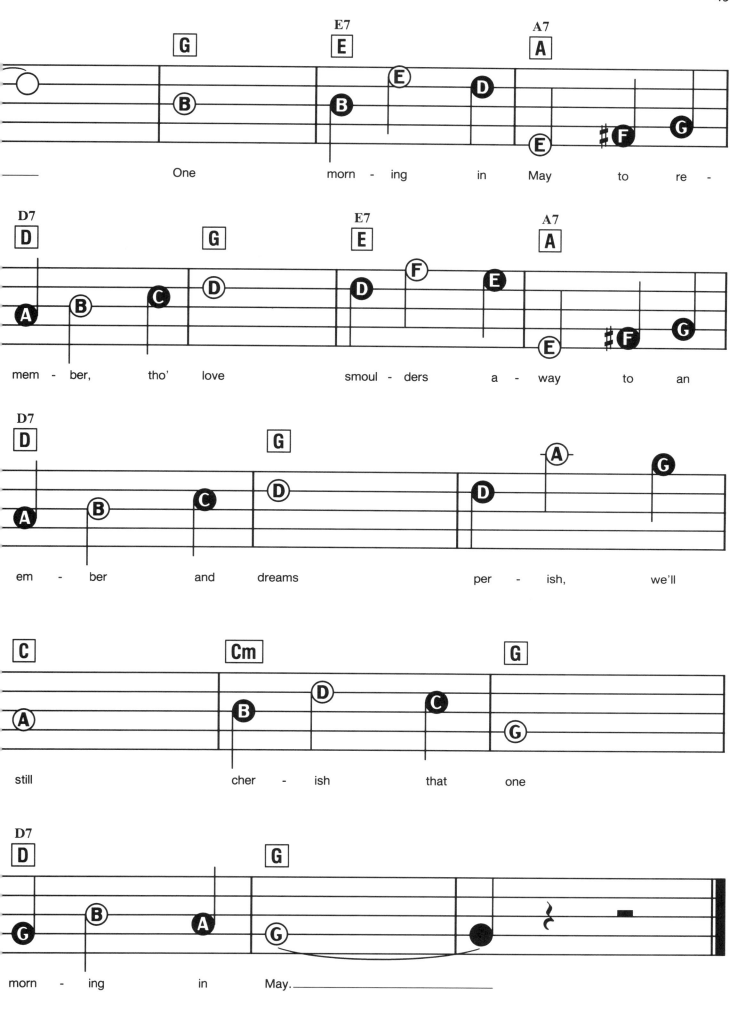

Laura

Registration 10
Rhythm: Fox-Trot or 8 Beat

Words by Johnny Mercer
Music by David Raksin

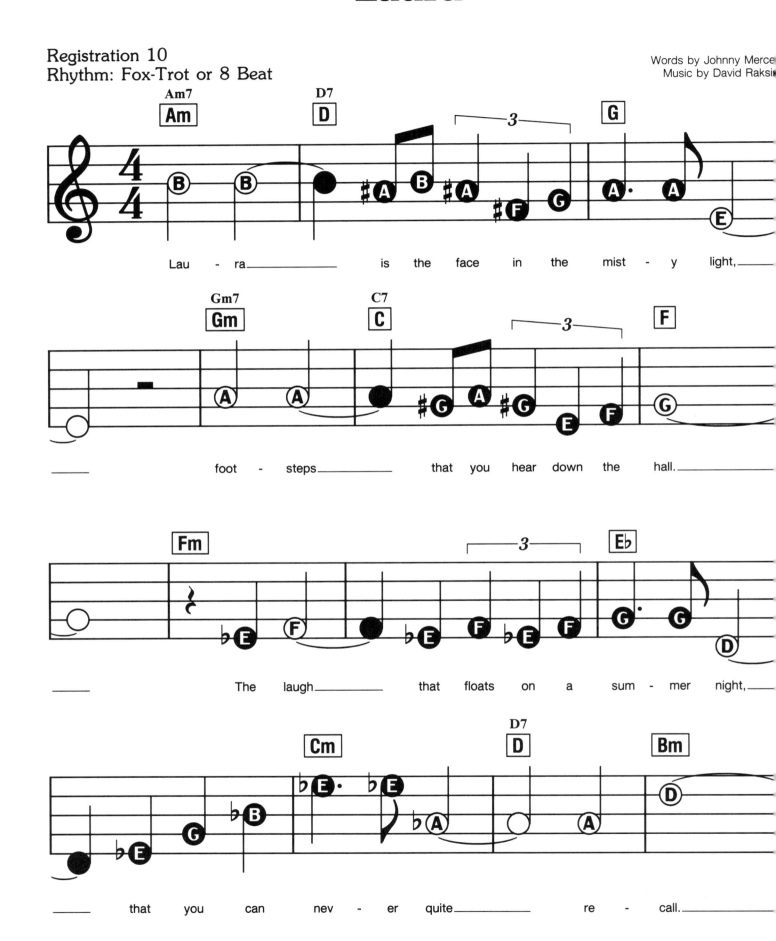

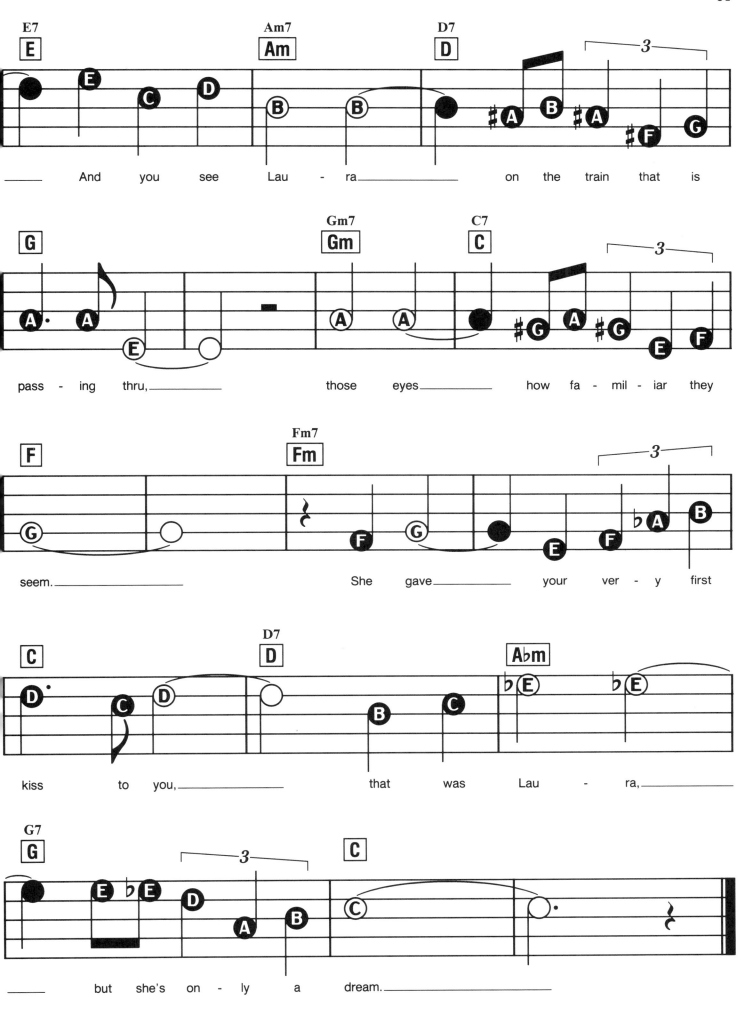

Louise

Registration 7
Rhythm: Swing or Shuffle

Words by Leo Robin
Music by Richard A. Whiting

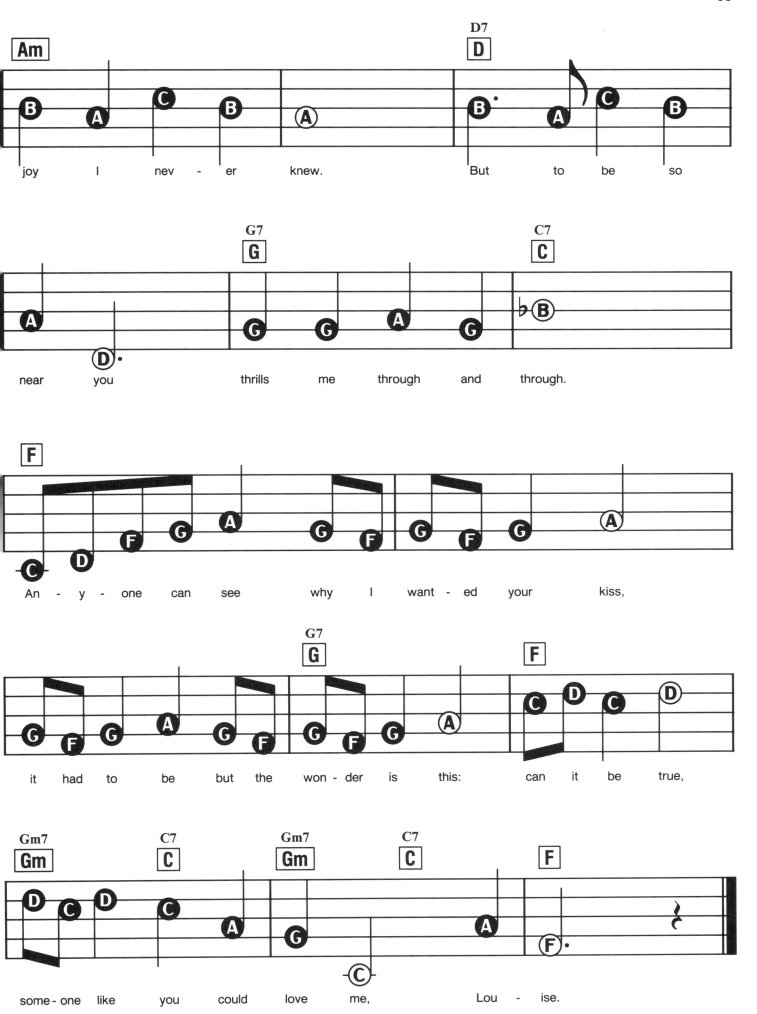

Love Is A Many Splendored Thing

Registration 9
Rhythm: Swing

Words by Paul Francis Webster
Music by Sammy Fain

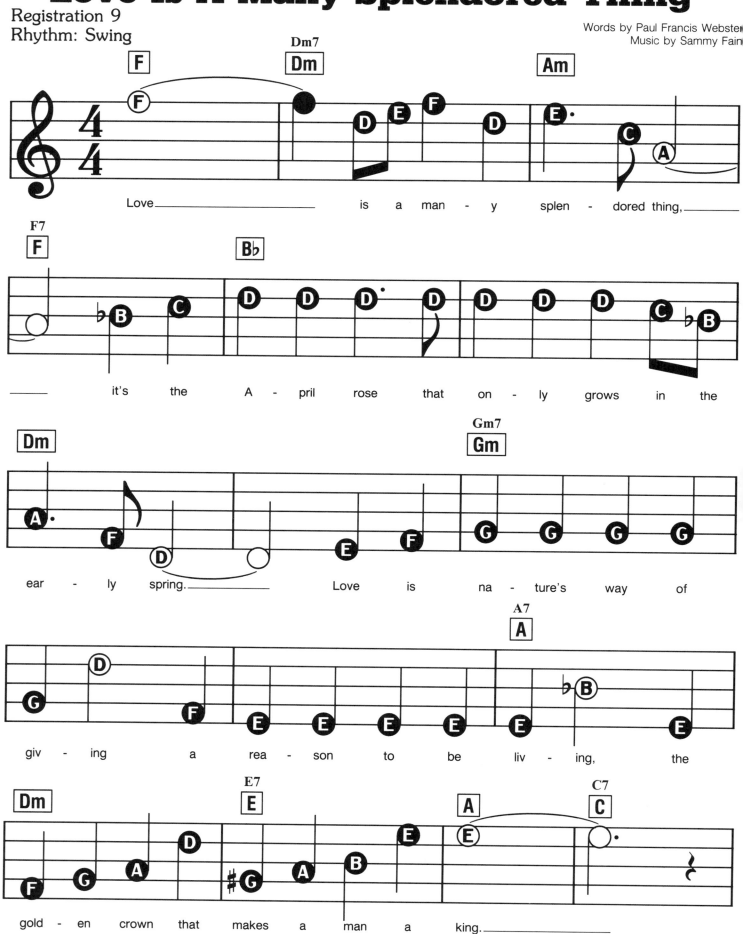

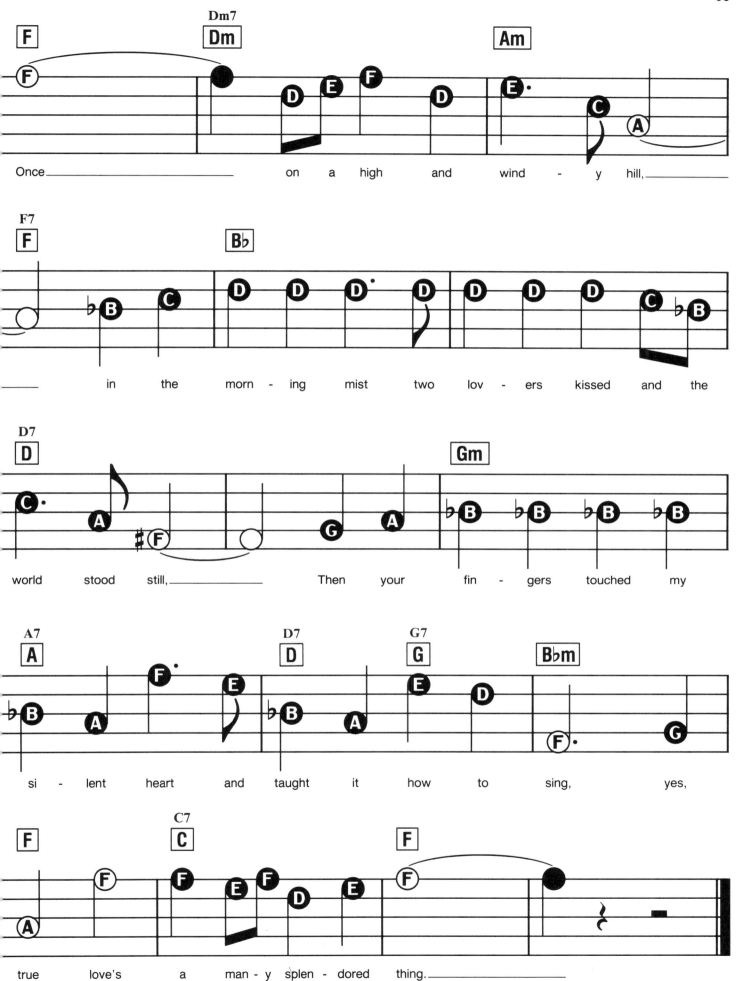

Love Is Just Around The Corner

Registration 7
Rhythm: Swing or Shuffle

Words and Music by
Leo Robin and Lewis E. Gensle

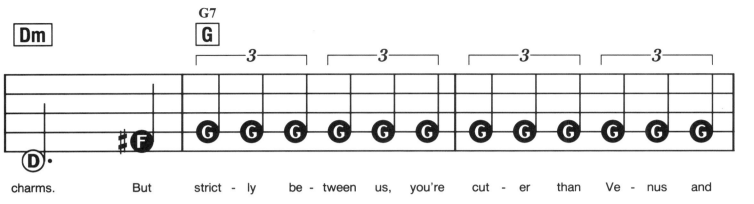

charms.   But   strict - ly   be - tween   us,   you're   cut - er   than   Ve - nus   and

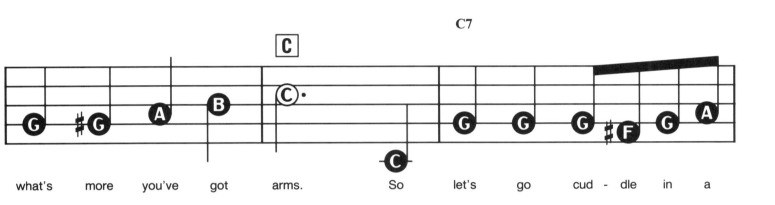

what's   more   you've   got   arms.   So   let's   go   cud - dle   in   a

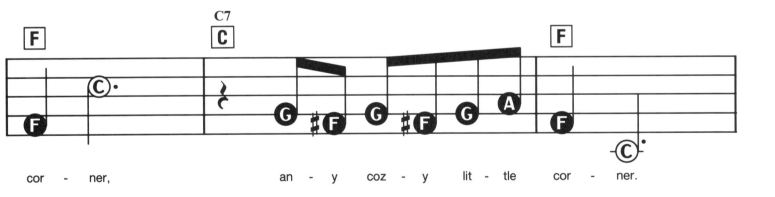

cor - ner,   an - y   coz - y   lit - tle   cor - ner.

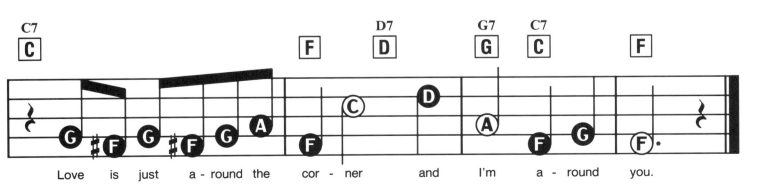

Love   is   just   a - round   the   cor - ner   and   I'm   a - round   you.

Love Me With All Your Heart
(Cuando Calienta El Sol)

Registration 7
Rhythm: Latin or Rhumba

English Lyric by Sunny Skylar
Music by Carlos Rigual and Carlos A. Martinoli

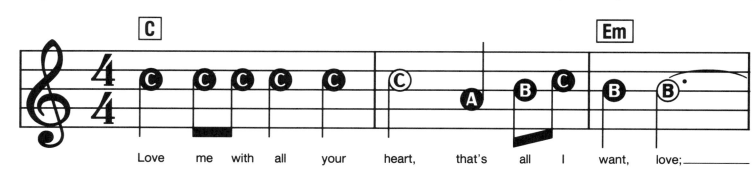

Love me with all your heart, that's all I want, love;

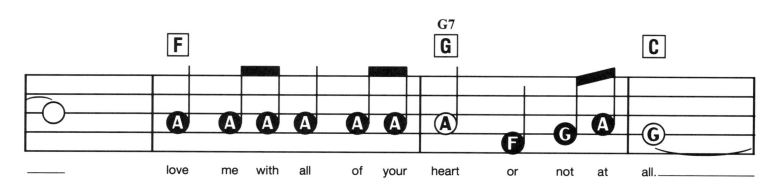

love me with all of your heart or not at all.

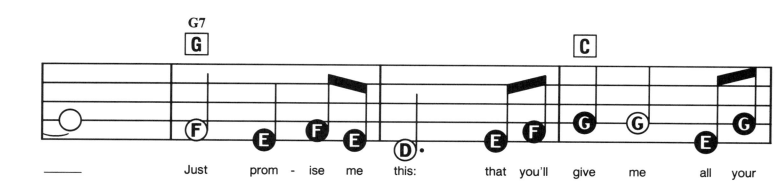

Just prom - ise me this: that you'll give me all your

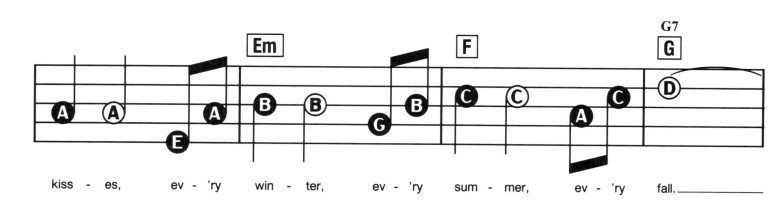

kiss - es, ev - 'ry win - ter, ev - 'ry sum - mer, ev - 'ry fall.

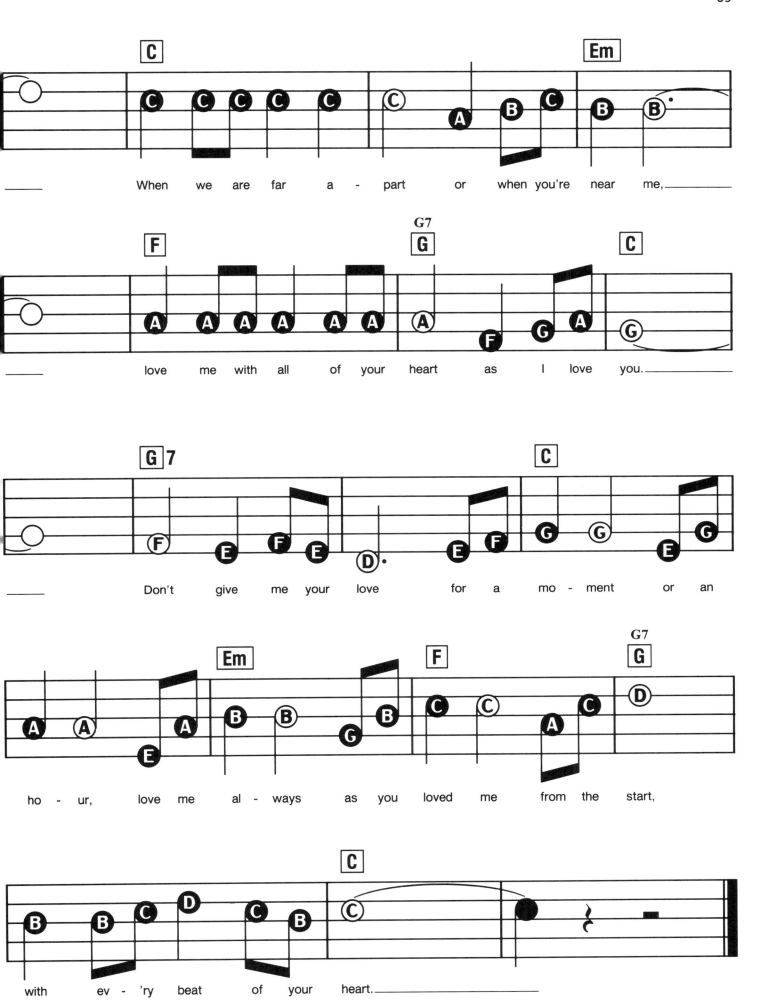

Magic Moments

Registration 9
Rhythm: Swing or Shuffle

Lyric by Hal David
Music by Burt Bacharach

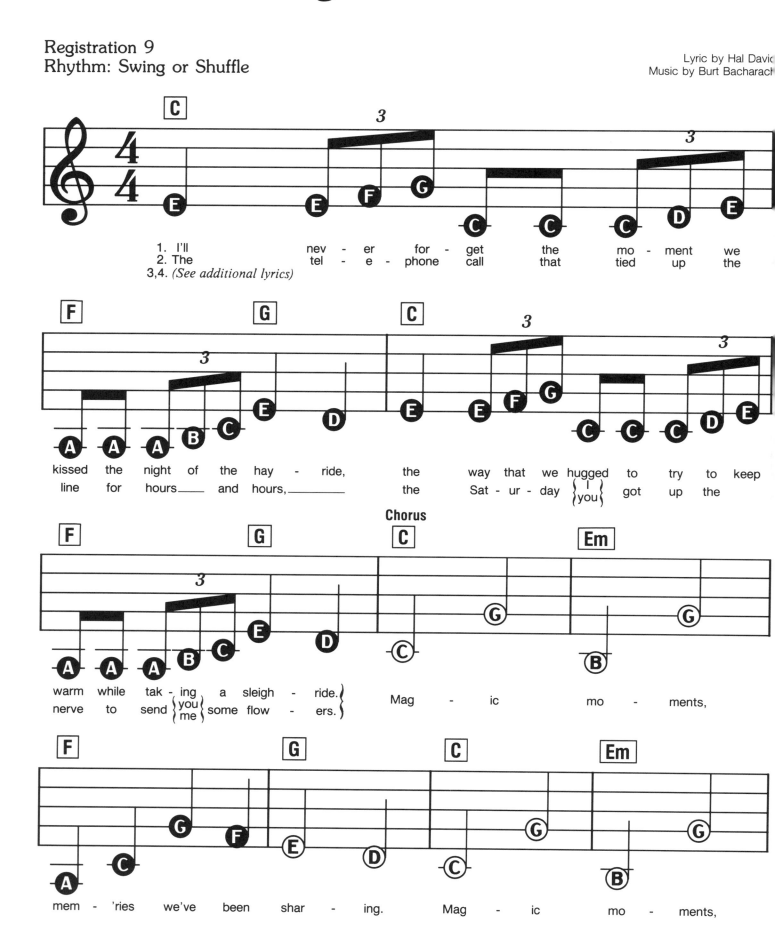

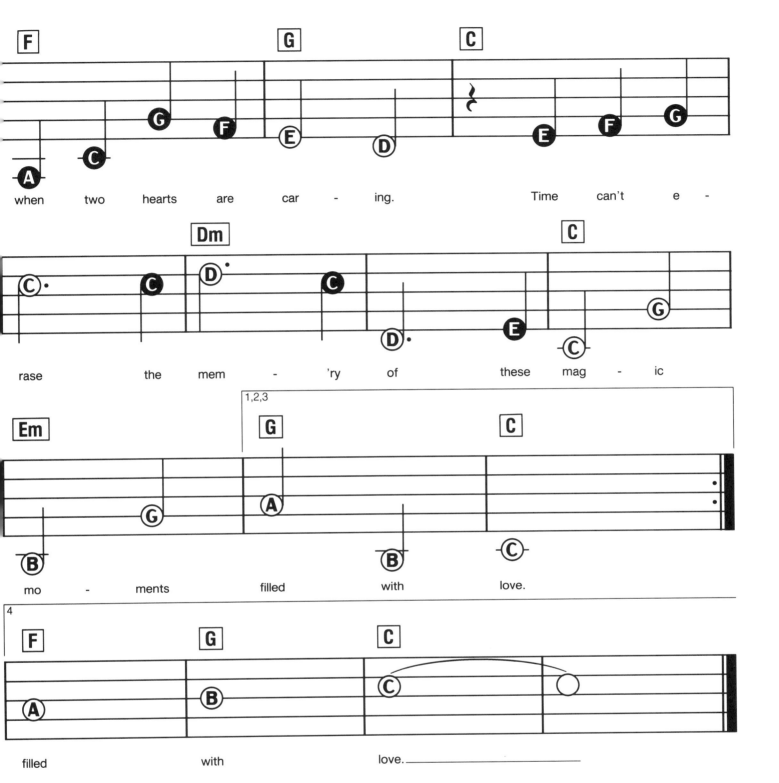

when two hearts are car - ing. Time can't e -

rase the mem - 'ry of these mag - ic

mo - ments filled with love.

filled with love._____

Additional Lyrics

3. The way that we cheered whenever our team was scoring a touchdown,
   The time that the floor fell out of { my / your } car when { I / you } put the clutch down;
   (To Chorus)

4. The penny arcade, the games that we played, the fun and the prizes,
   The Halloween hop when ev'ryone came in funny disguises;
   (To Chorus)

Mona Lisa

Registration 9
Rhythm: Swing or 8 Beat

By Jay Livingston
and Ray Evans

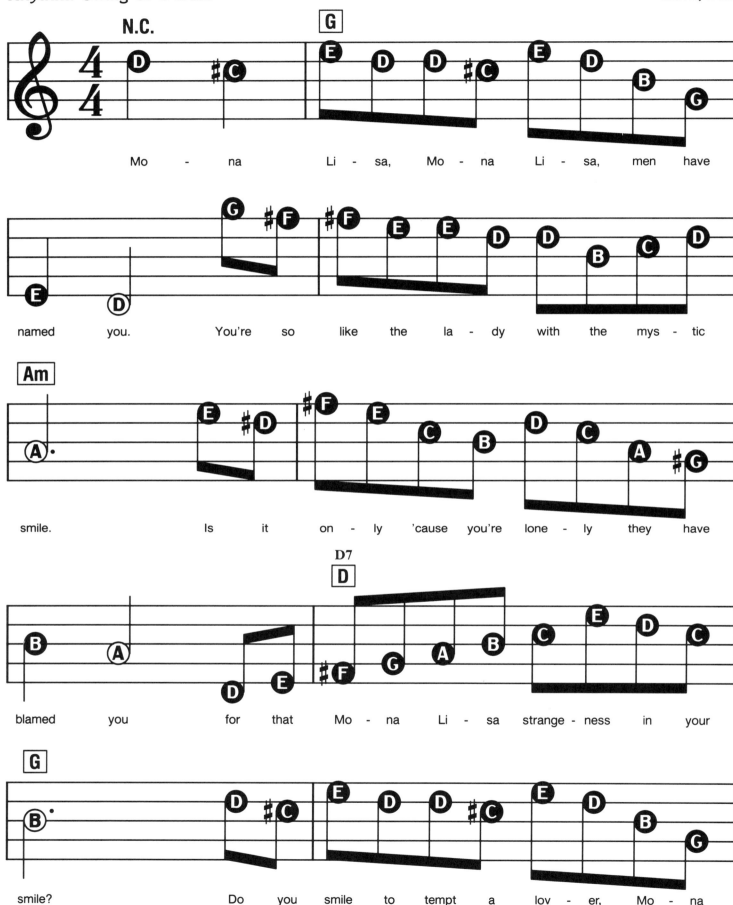

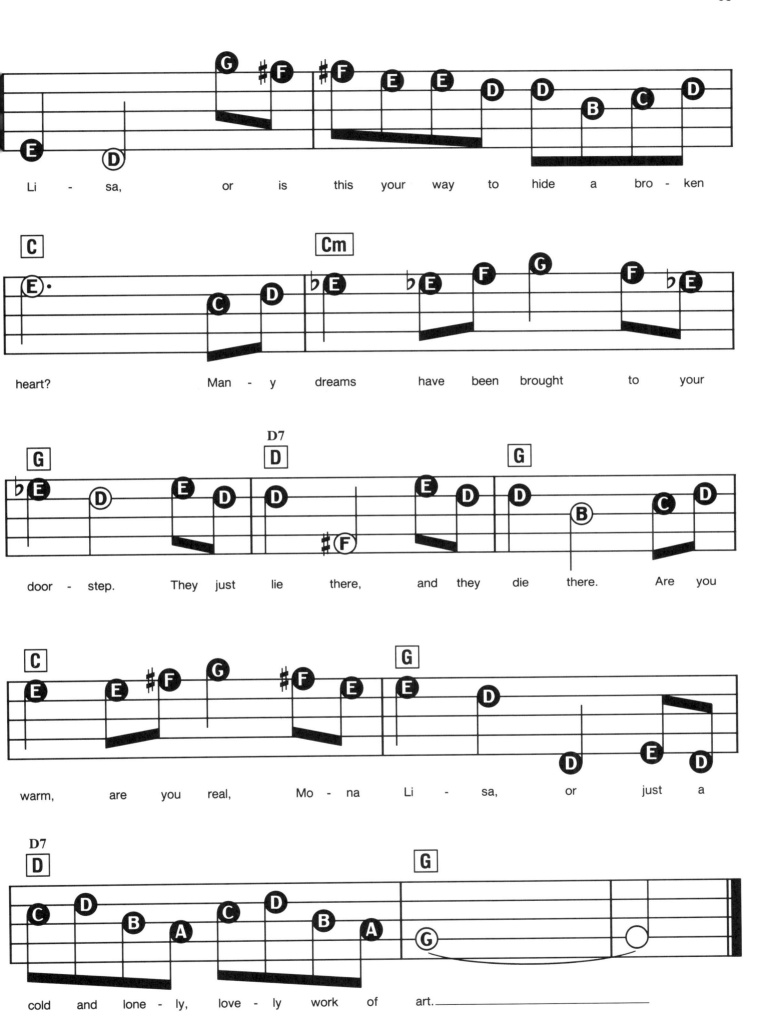

Moonglow

Registration 2
Rhythm: Fox Trot

Words and Music by Will Hudson
Eddie DeLange and Irving Mills

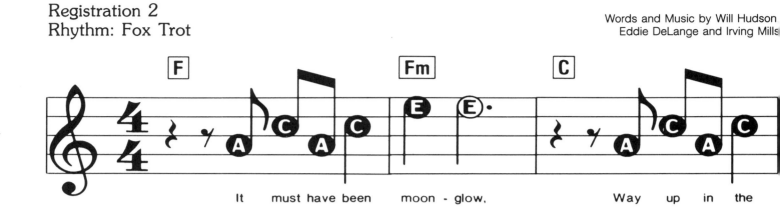

It must have been moon-glow, Way up in the

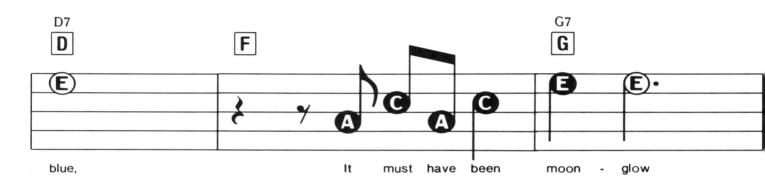

blue, It must have been moon - glow

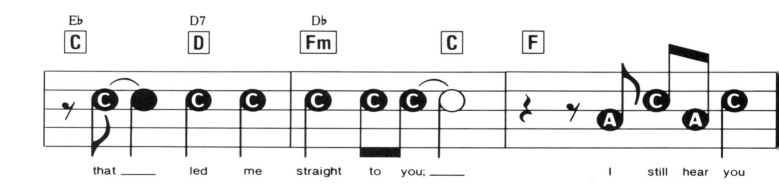

that _____ led me straight to you; _____ I still hear you

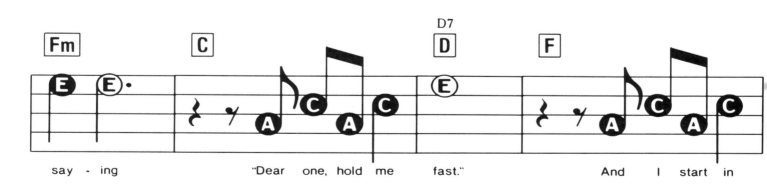

say - ing "Dear one, hold me fast." And I start in

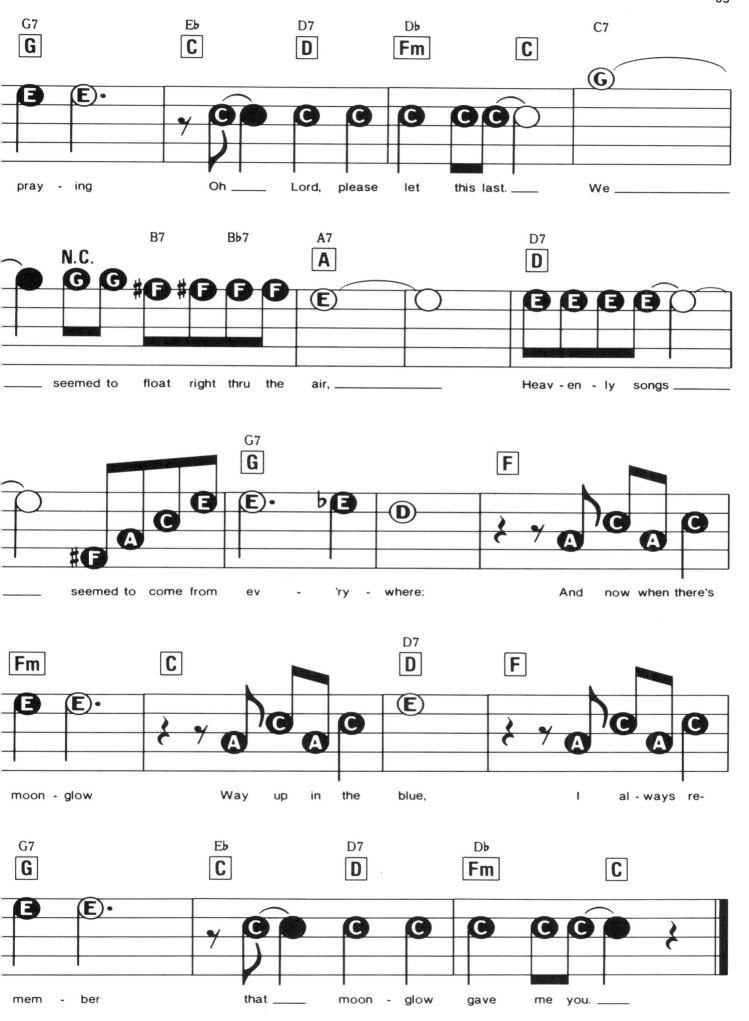

My Old Flame

Registration 4
Rhythm: Swing

By Arthur Johnst
and Sam Cosl

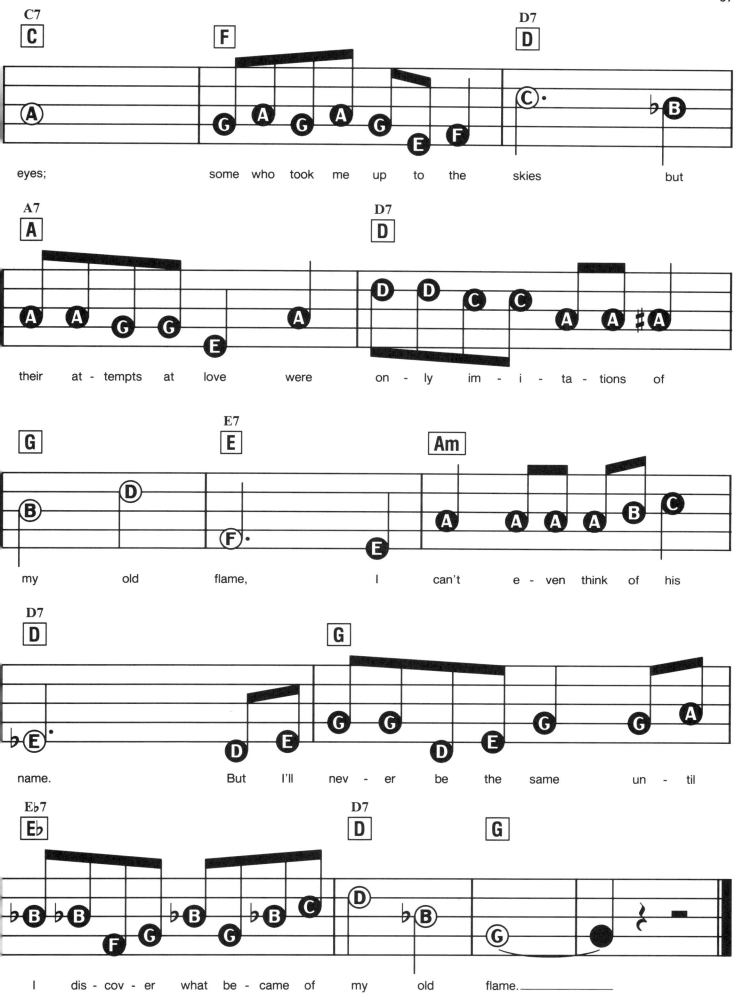

One O'Clock Jump

Registration 7
Rhythm: Swing or Shuffle

By Count Basie

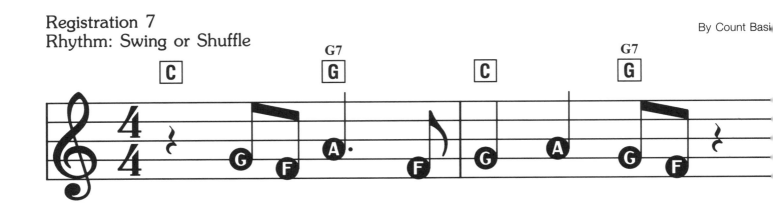

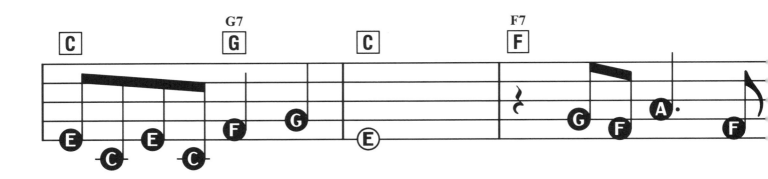

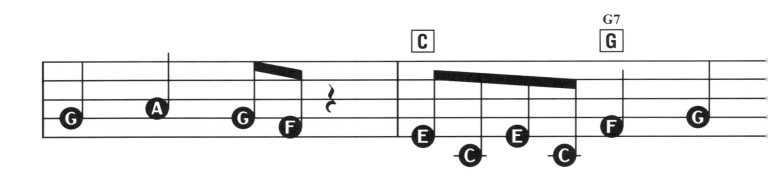

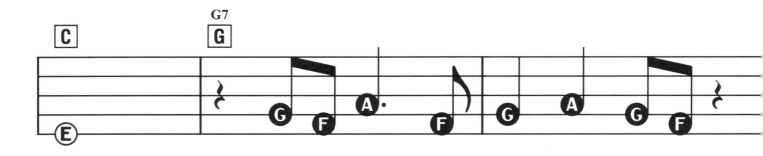

Out Of Nowhere

Registration 9
Rhythm: Fox-Trot or Swing

Words and Music by
Edward Heyman and Johnny Green

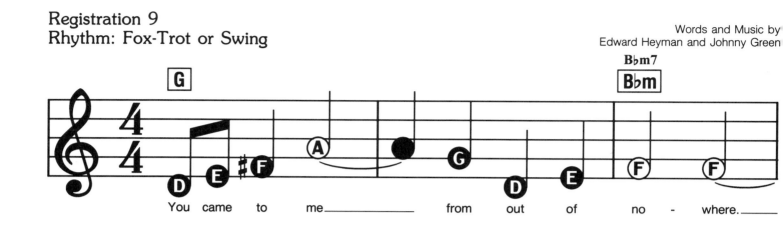

You came to me____ from out of no - where.

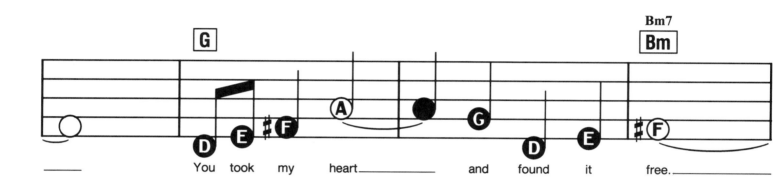

____ You took my heart____ and found it free.____

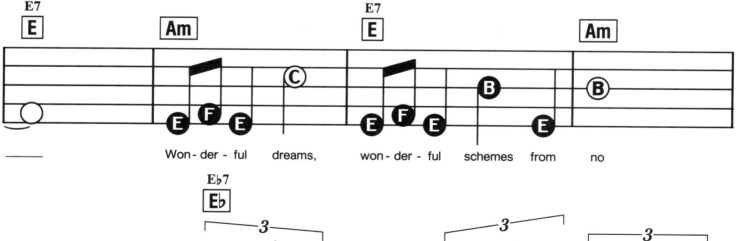

____ Won - der - ful dreams, won - der - ful schemes from no

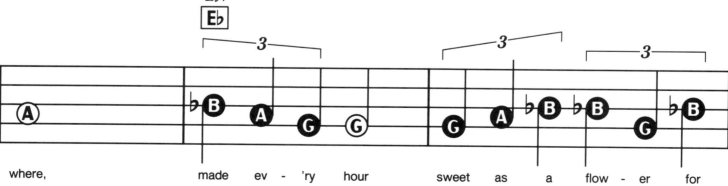

where, made ev - 'ry hour sweet as a flow - er for

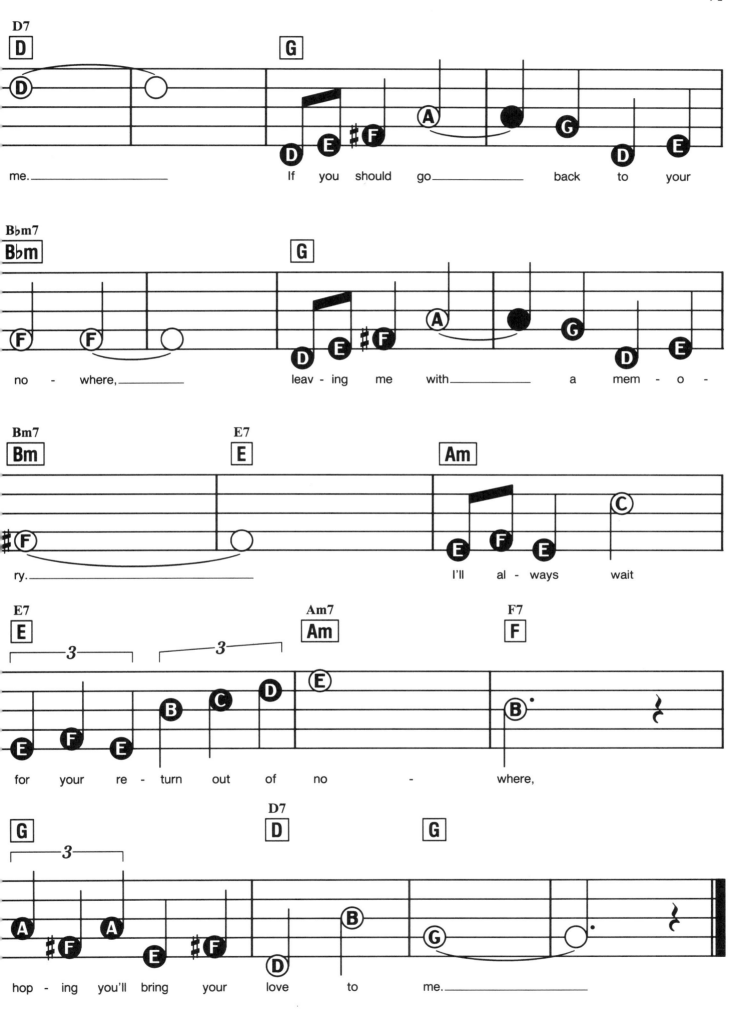

Over The Rainbow

Registration 5
Rhythm: Fox Trot or Swing

Music by Harold Arlen
Lyric by E. Y. Harburg

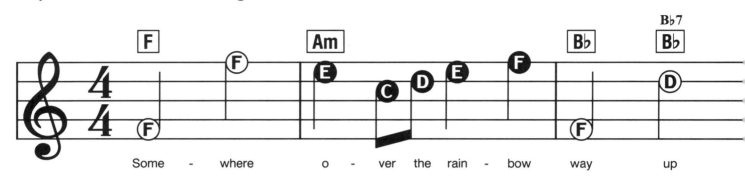

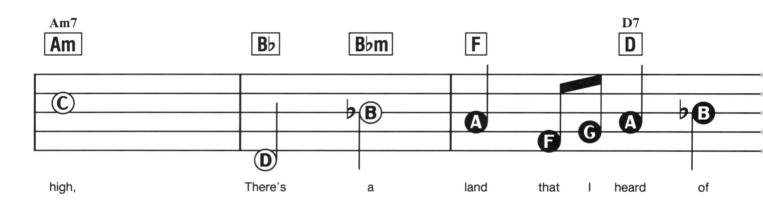

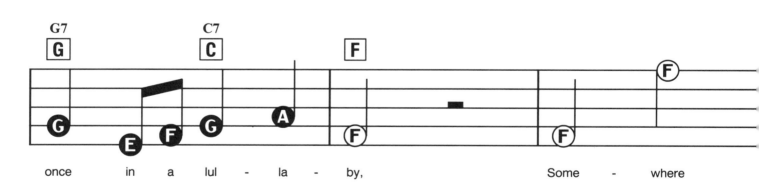

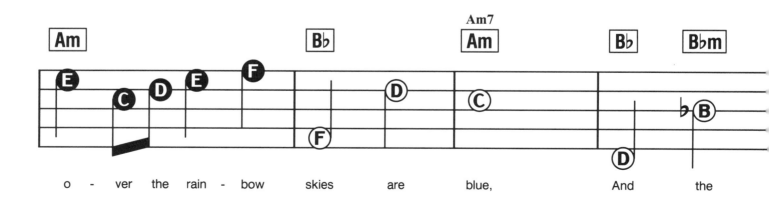

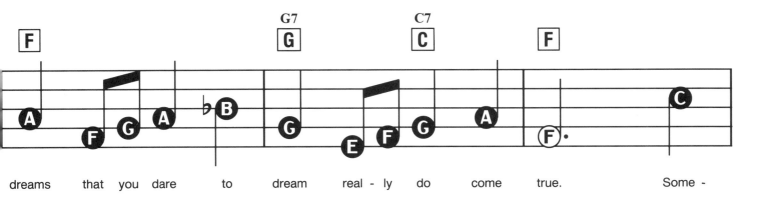

dreams that you dare to dream real - ly do come true. Some -

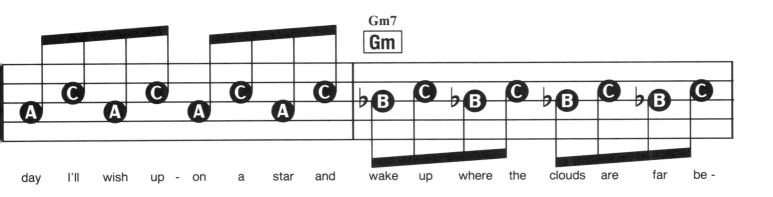

day I'll wish up - on a star and wake up where the clouds are far be -

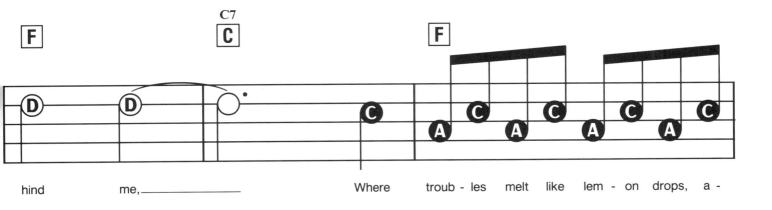

hind me,_____ Where troub - les melt like lem - on drops, a -

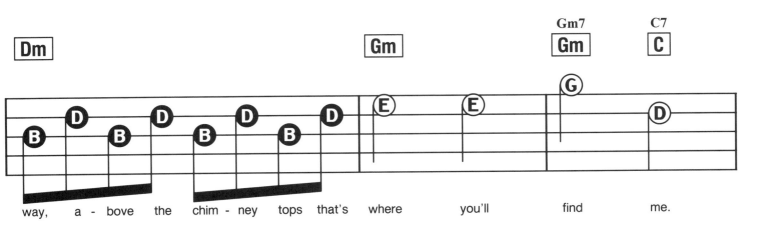

way, a - bove the chim - ney tops that's where you'll find me.

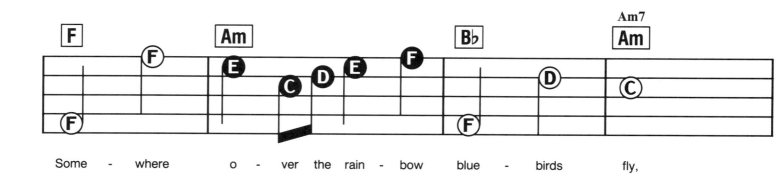

Some - where   o - ver the rain - bow blue - birds   fly,

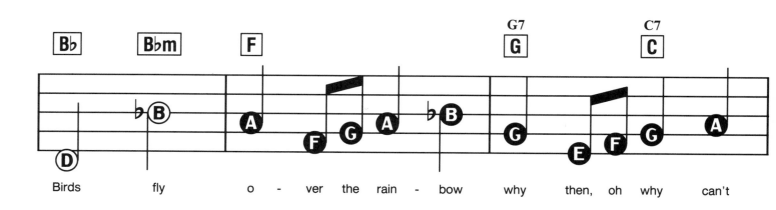

Birds   fly   o - ver the rain - bow   why   then, oh why   can't

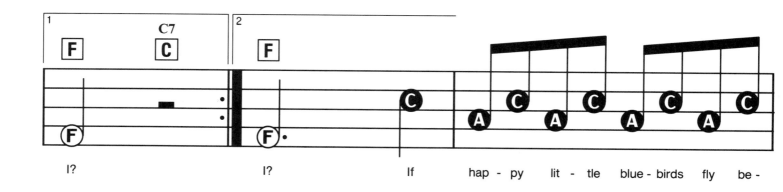

I?   I?   If   hap - py lit - tle blue - birds fly be -

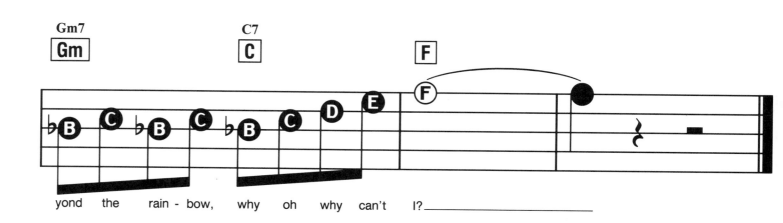

yond   the   rain - bow,   why   oh   why   can't   I?

Thanks For The Memory
(From "BIG BROADCAST OF 1938")

Registration 3
Rhythm: Swing

Words and Music by Leo Robin
and Ralph Rainger

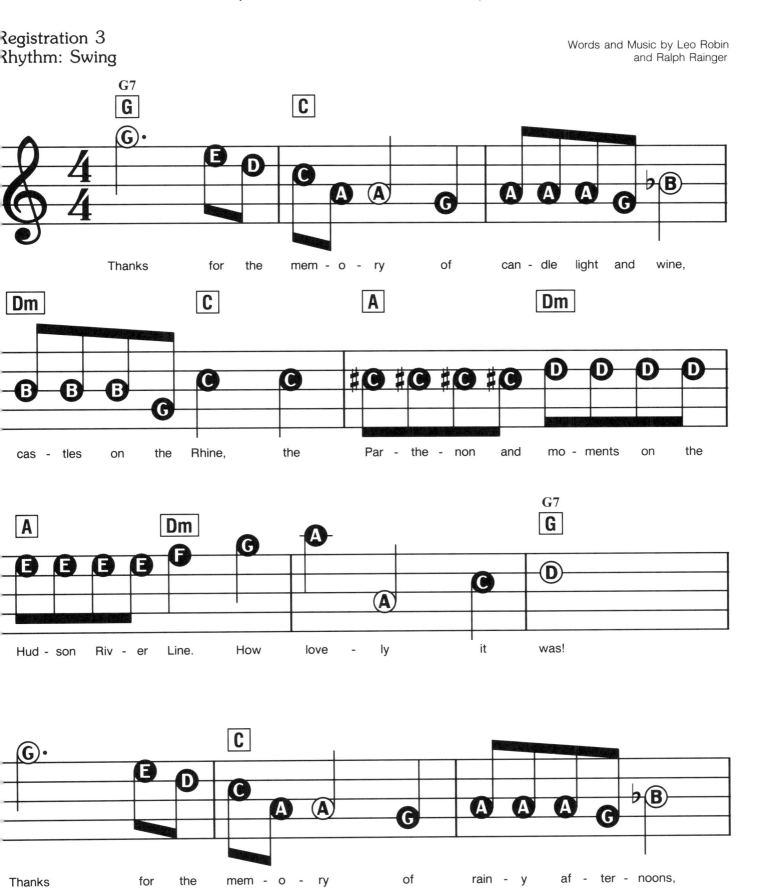

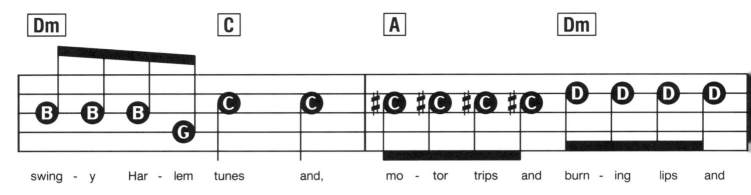

swing - y Har - lem tunes and, mo - tor trips and burn - ing lips and

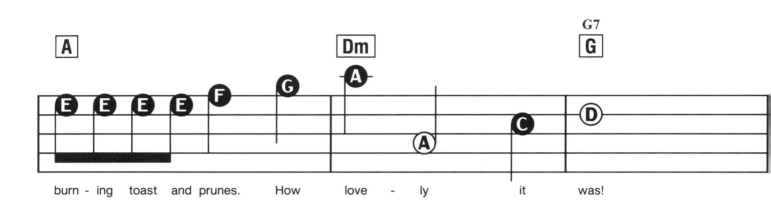

burn - ing toast and prunes. How love - ly it was!

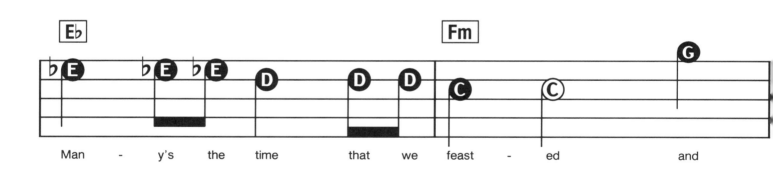

Man - y's the time that we feast - ed and

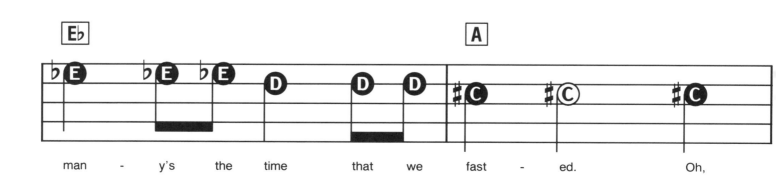

man - y's the time that we fast - ed. Oh,

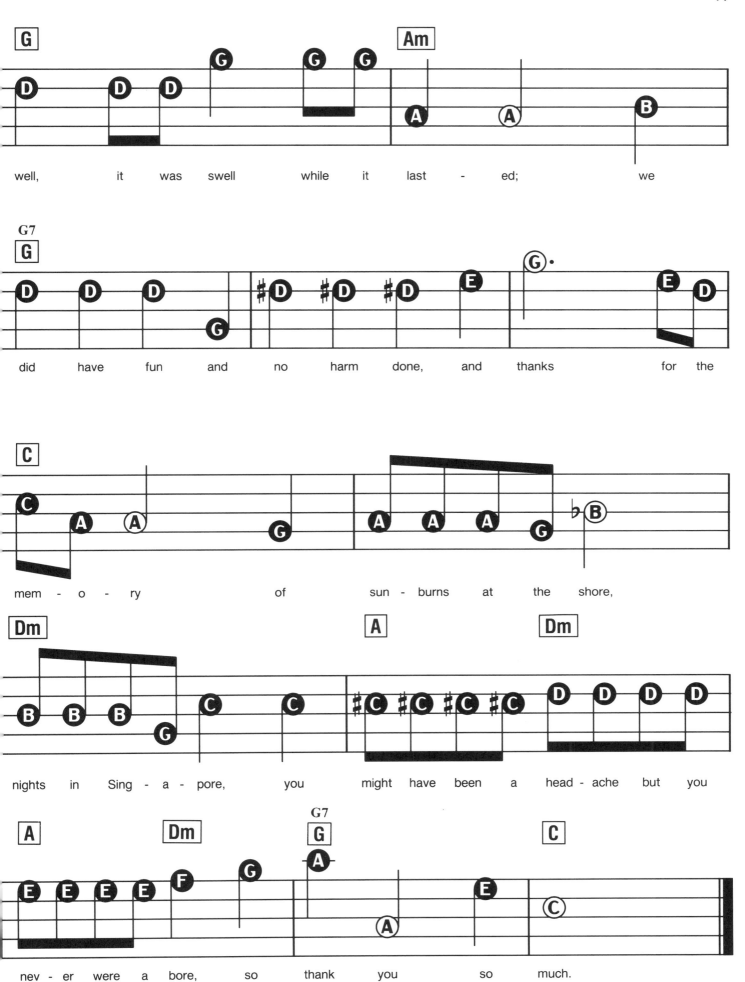

Ramona

Registration 5
Rhythm: Waltz

Words by L. Wolfe Gilbe[rt]
Music by Mabel Wayn[e]

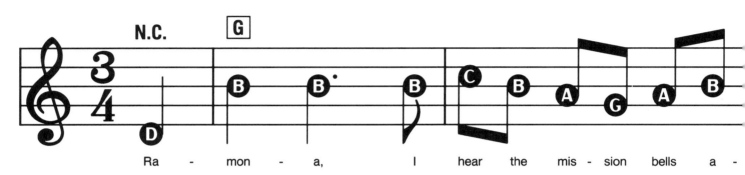

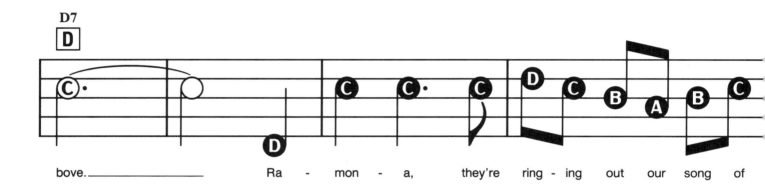

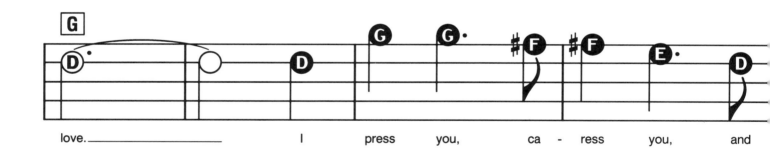

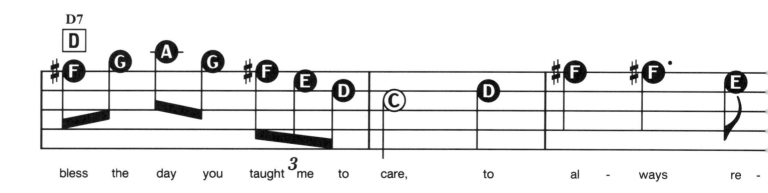

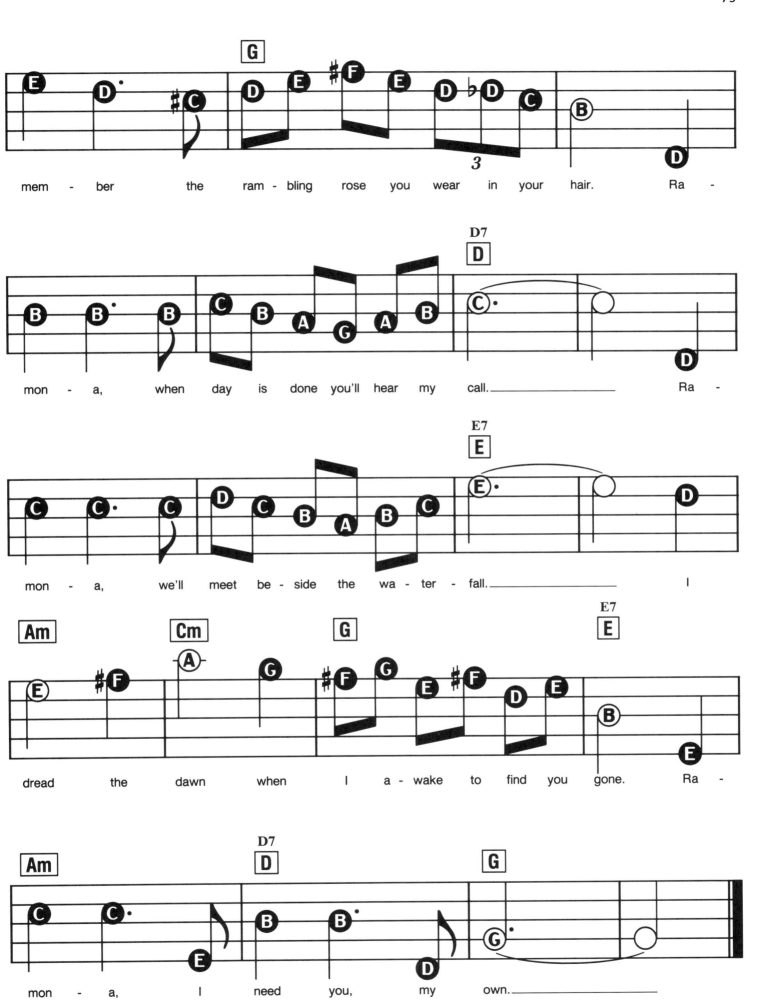

Release Me

Registration 1
Rhythm: Country

Words and Music by
Eddie Miller and W.S. Stevenson

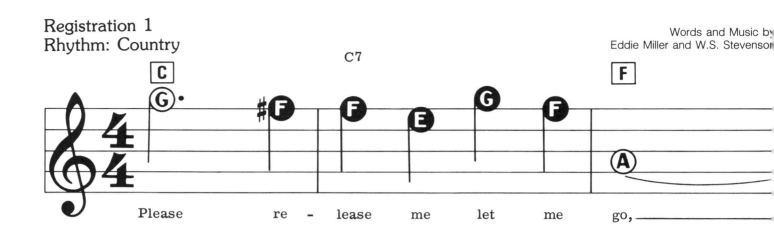

Please　re - lease　me　let　me　go, _____

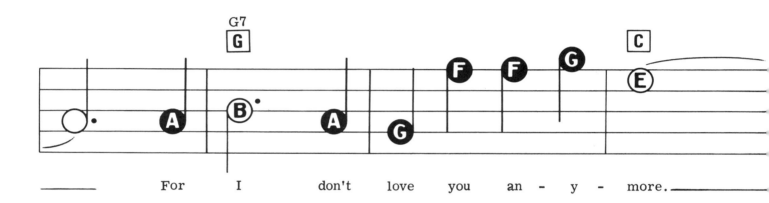

_____　For　I　don't　love　you　an - y - more. _____

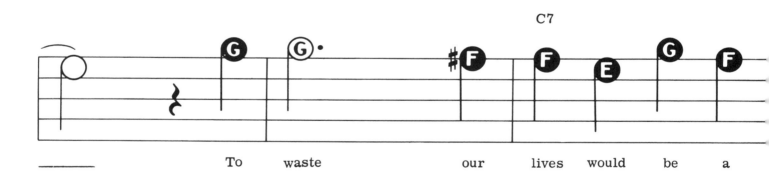

_____　To　waste　our　lives　would　be　a

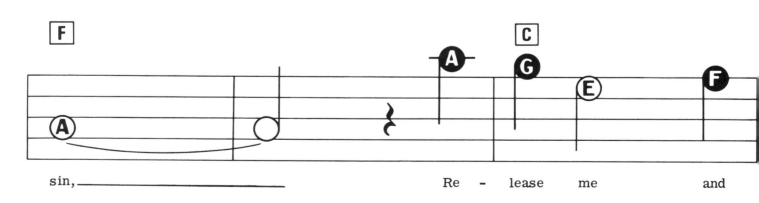

sin, _____　Re - lease　me　and

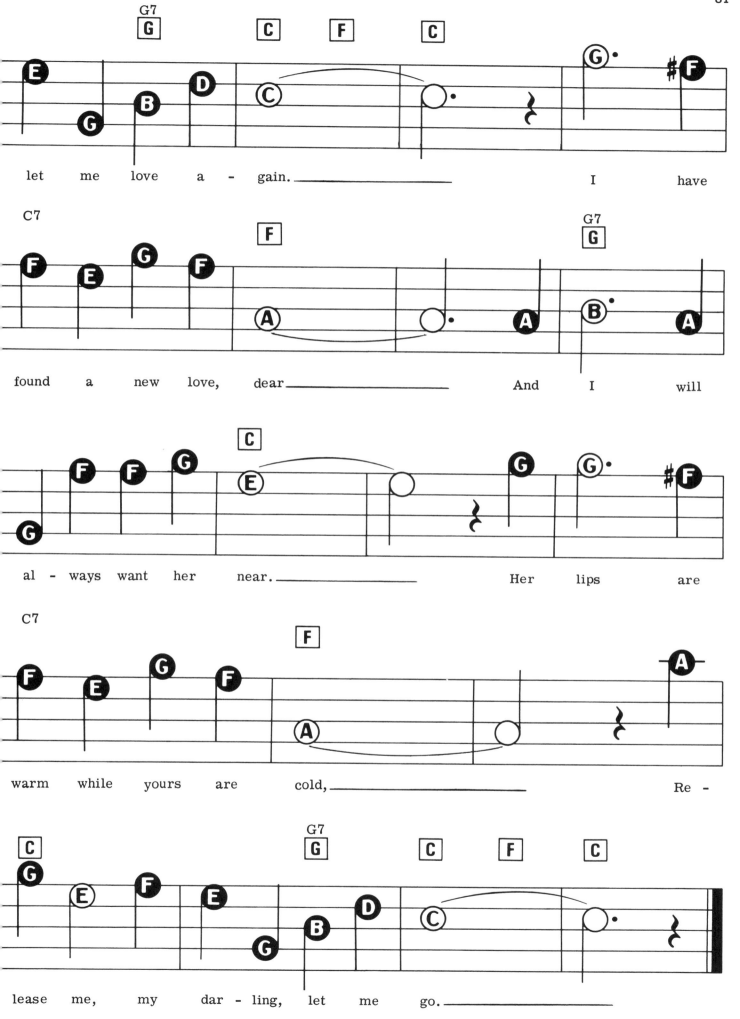

Rum And Coca-Cola

Words by Morey Amsterdam
Additional Lyrics by Al Stillman
Music by Jeri Sullivan and Paul Baron

Registration 7
Rhythm: Latin, Calypso, or Rock

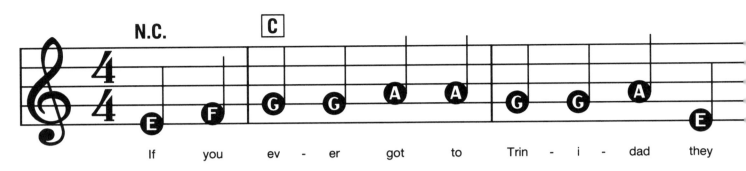

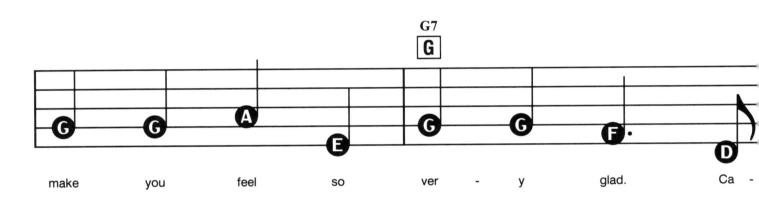

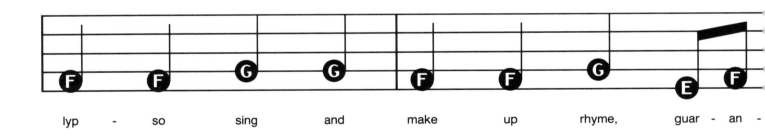

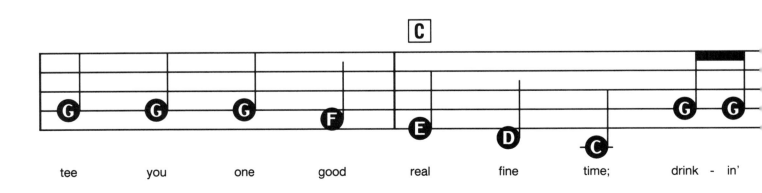

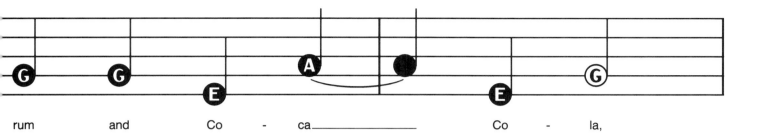

rum and Co - ca_____ Co - la,

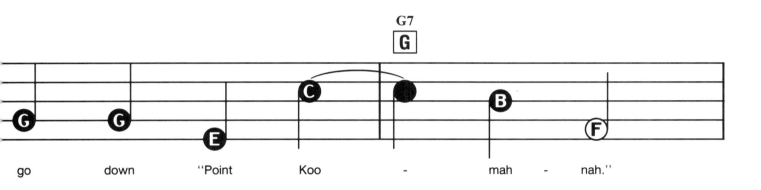

go down "Point Koo - mah - nah."

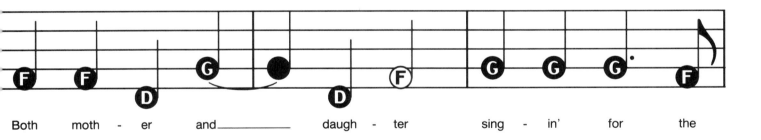

Both moth - er and_____ daugh - ter sing - in' for the

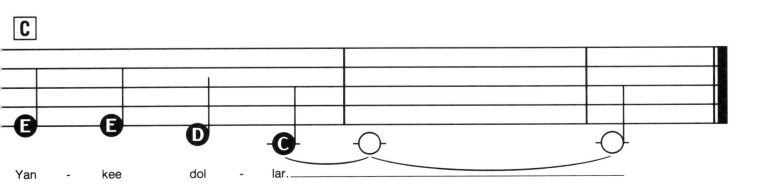

Yan - kee dol - lar._____

Shangri-La

Registration 2
Rhythm: Swing or Pops

Words by Carl Sigma[?]
Music by Matt Malneck and Robert Maxw[?]

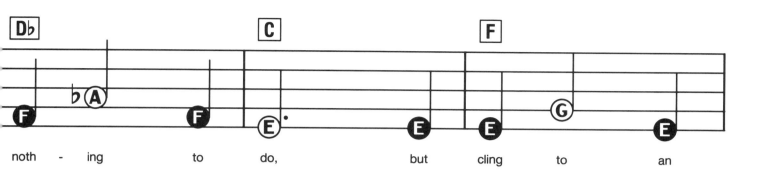

noth - ing   to   do,   but   cling   to   an

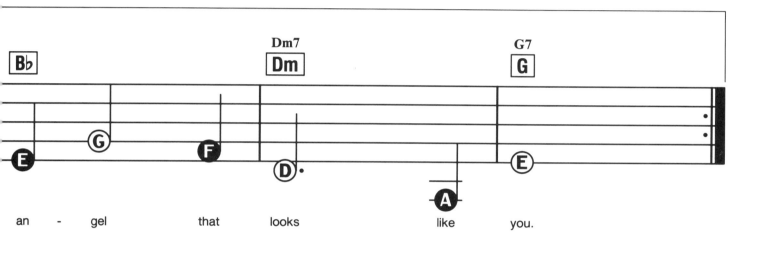

an - gel   that   looks   like   you.

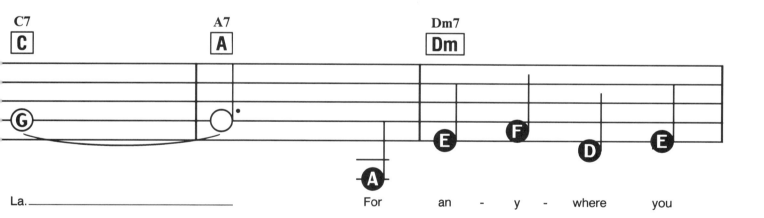

La.   For   an - y - where   you

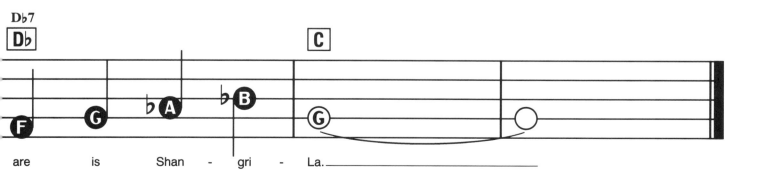

are   is   Shan - gri - La.

Should I

Registration 4
Rhythm: Fox-Trot, Polka, or Pops

Words by Arthur Freed
Music by Nacio Herb Brown

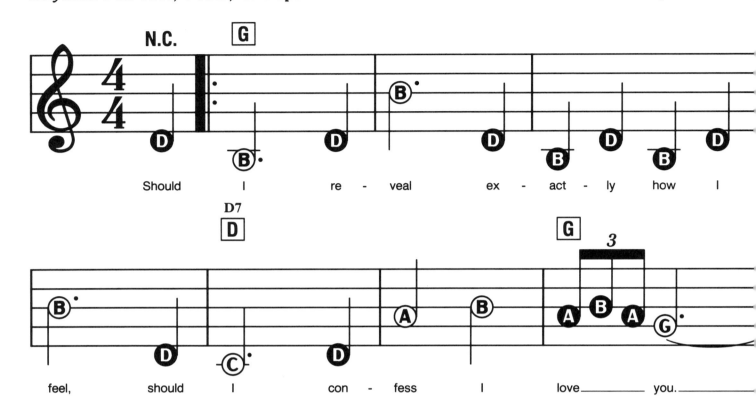

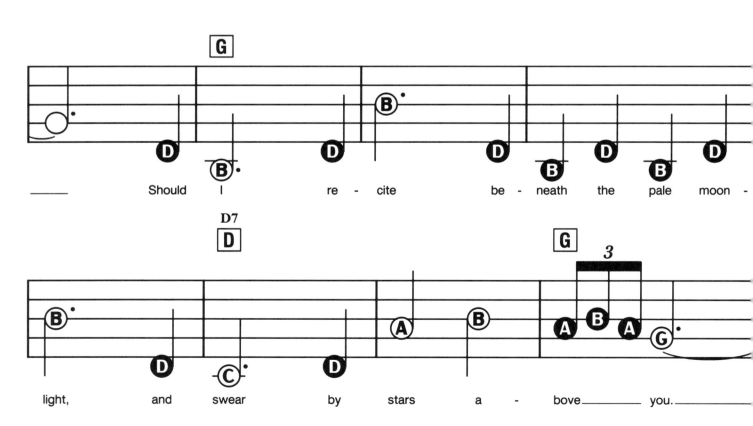

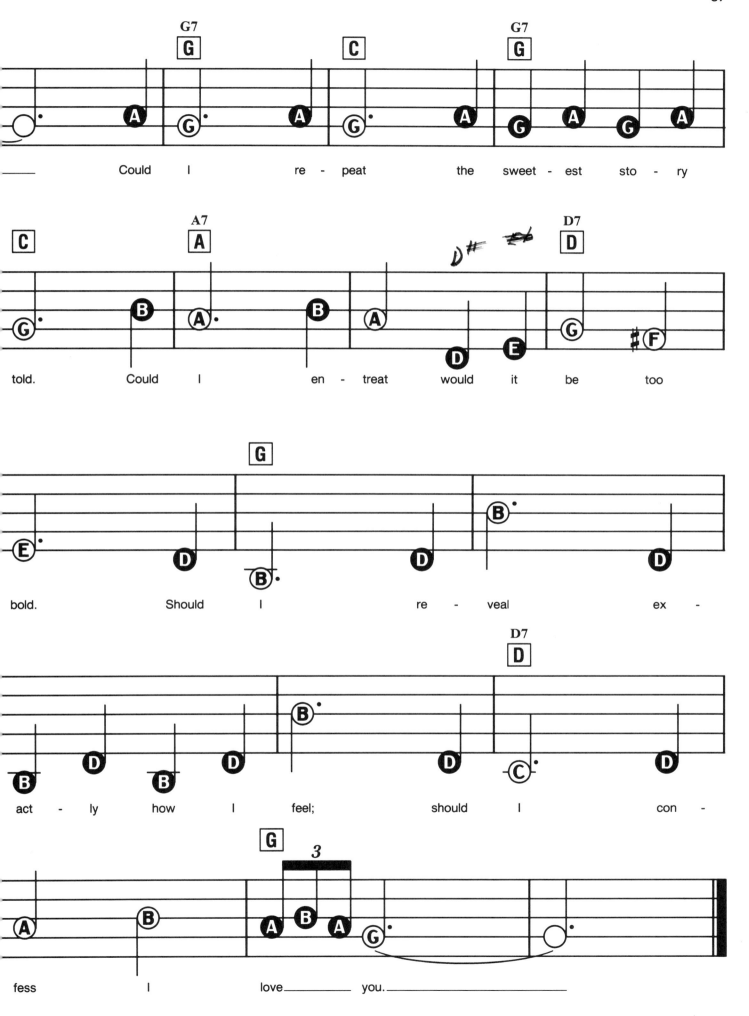

Singin' In The Rain

Registration 4
Rhythm: Swing

Words by Arthur Freed
Music by Nacio Herb Brown

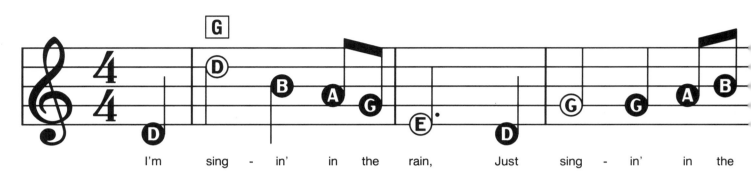

I'm sing - in' in the rain, Just sing - in' in the

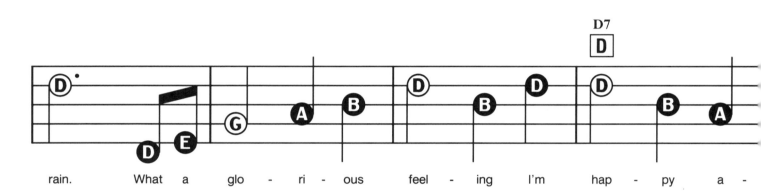

rain. What a glo - ri - ous feel - ing I'm hap - py a -

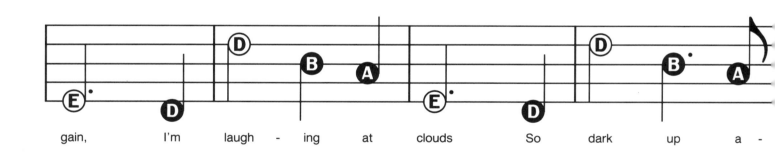

gain, I'm laugh - ing at clouds So dark up a -

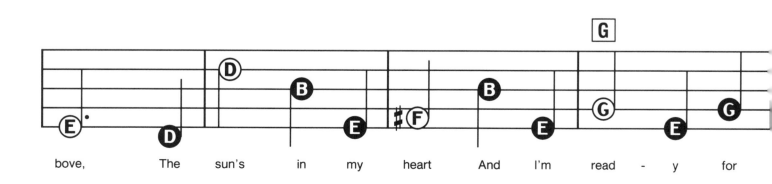

bove, The sun's in my heart And I'm read - y for

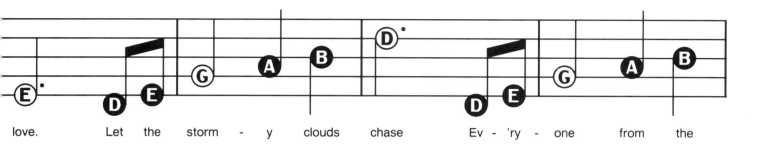

love. Let the storm - y clouds chase

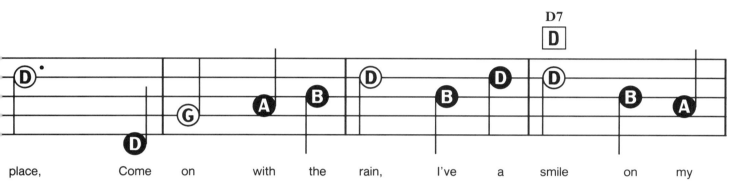

place, Come on with the rain, I've a smile on my

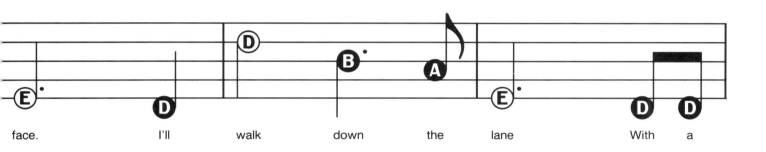

face. I'll walk down the lane With a

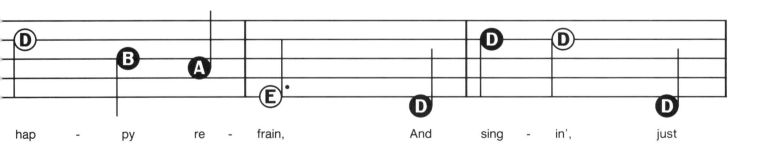

hap - py re - frain, And sing - in', just

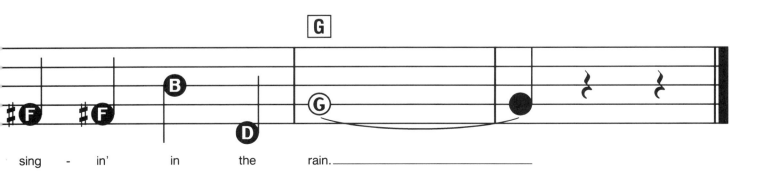

sing - in' in the rain.

Sleepy Time Gal

Registration 9
Rhythm: Swing

Words by Joseph R. Alden and Raymond B. Ega[n]
Music by Ange Lorenzo and Richard A. Whitin[g]

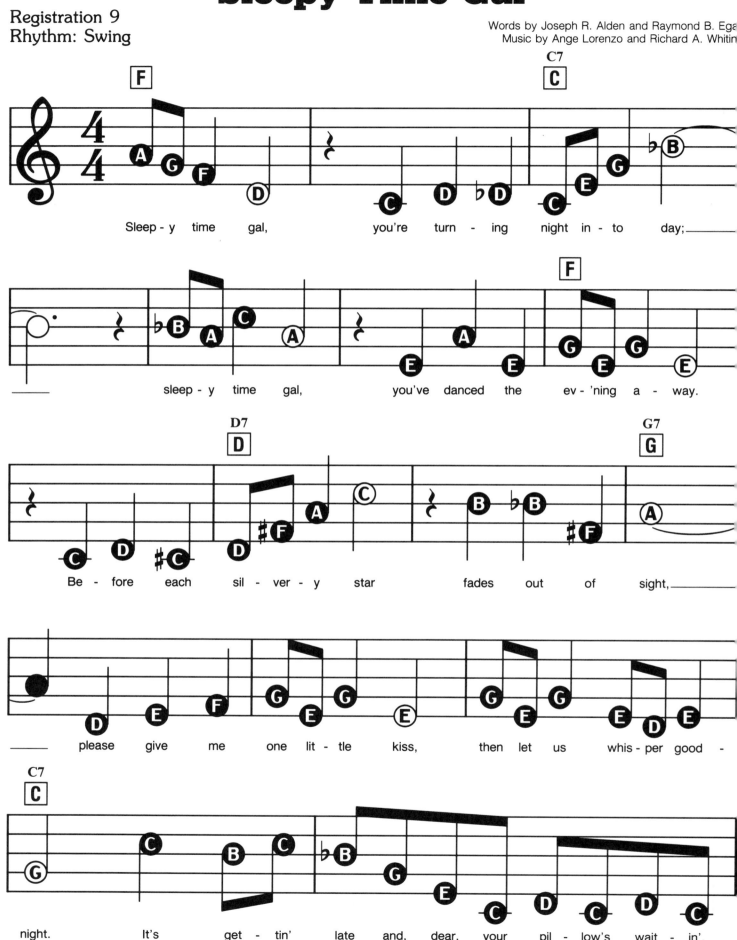

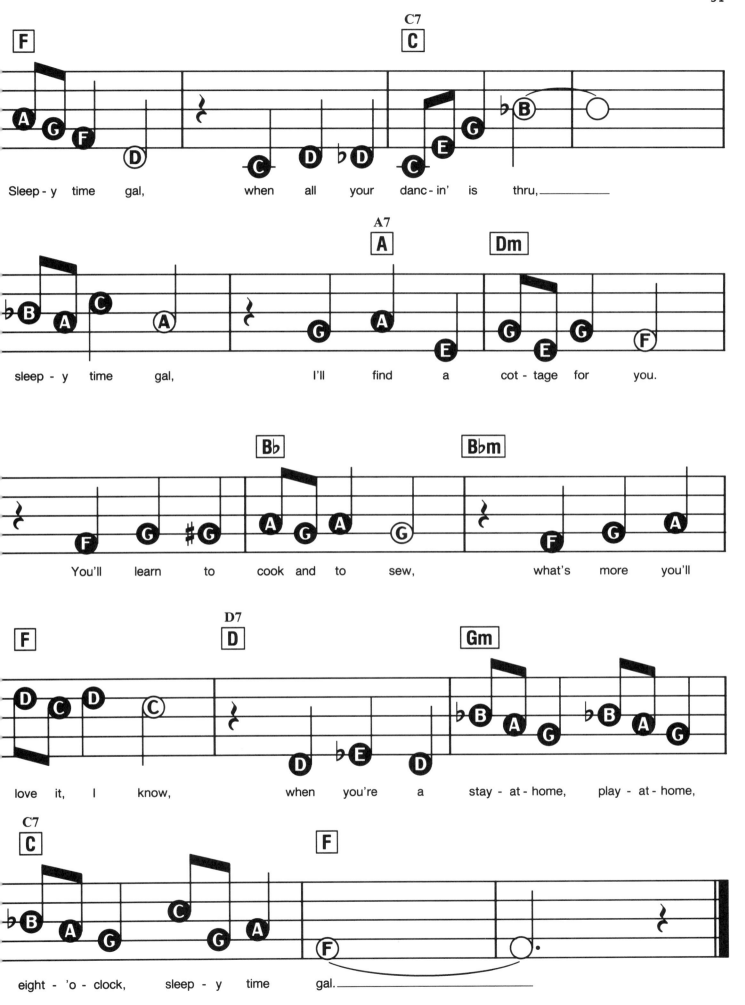

Softly, As I Leave You

Registration 1
Rhythm: Fox-Trot or 8-Beat

Original Italian Text by G. Calabres
English Lyric by Hal Shape
Music by A. DeVit

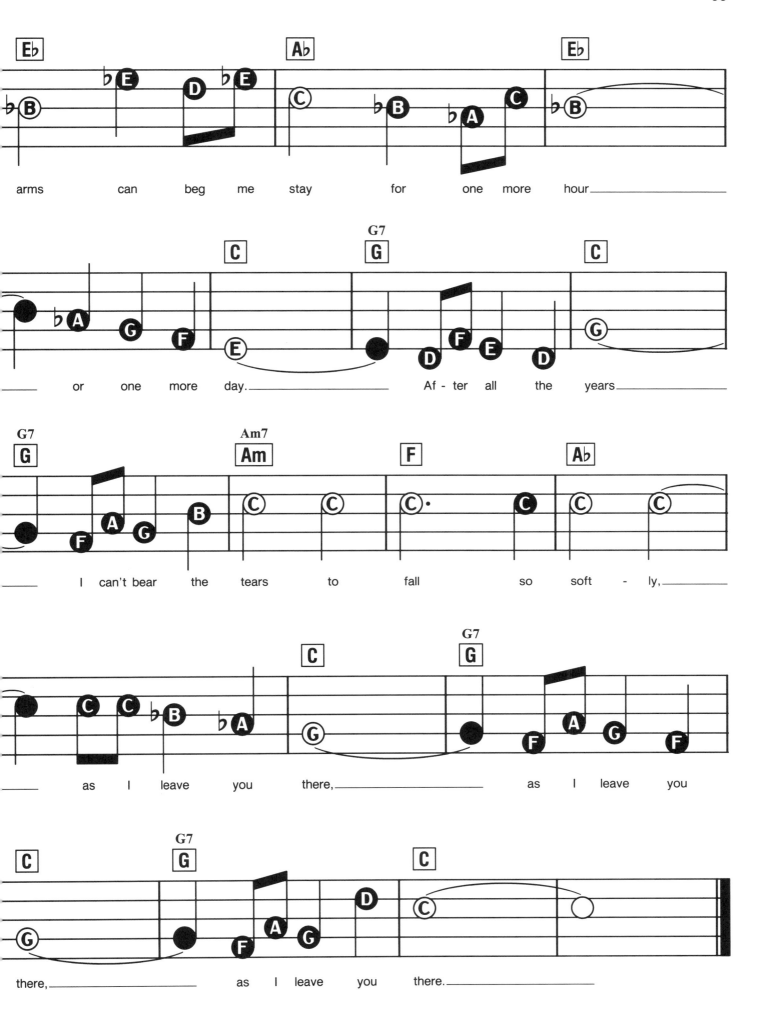

Temptation

Registration 9
Rhythm: Latin or Bossa Nova

Words by Arthur Free
Music by Nacio Herb Brow

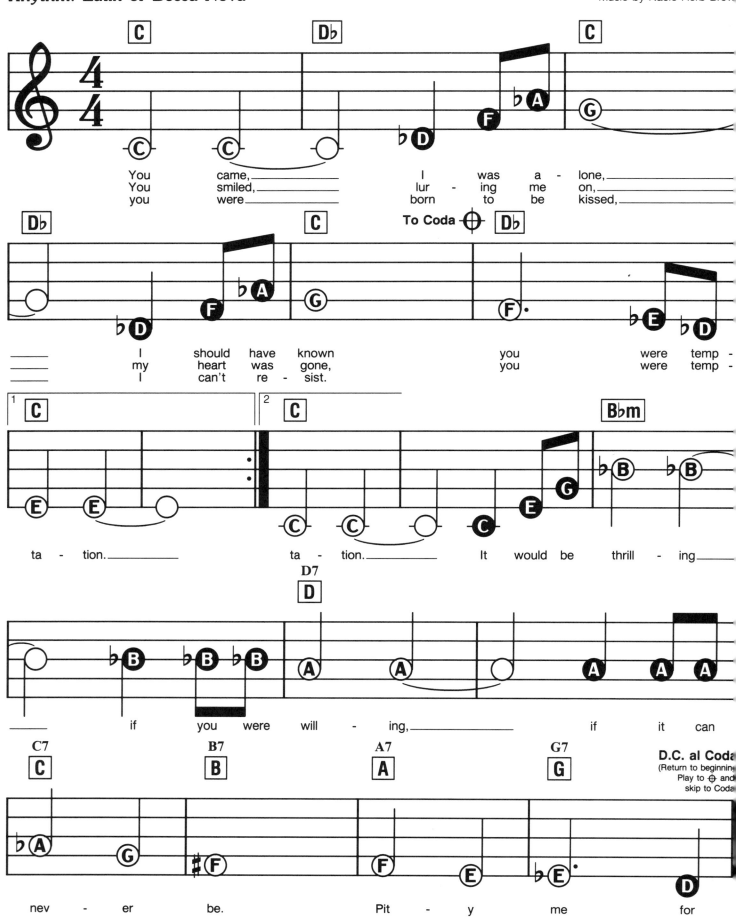

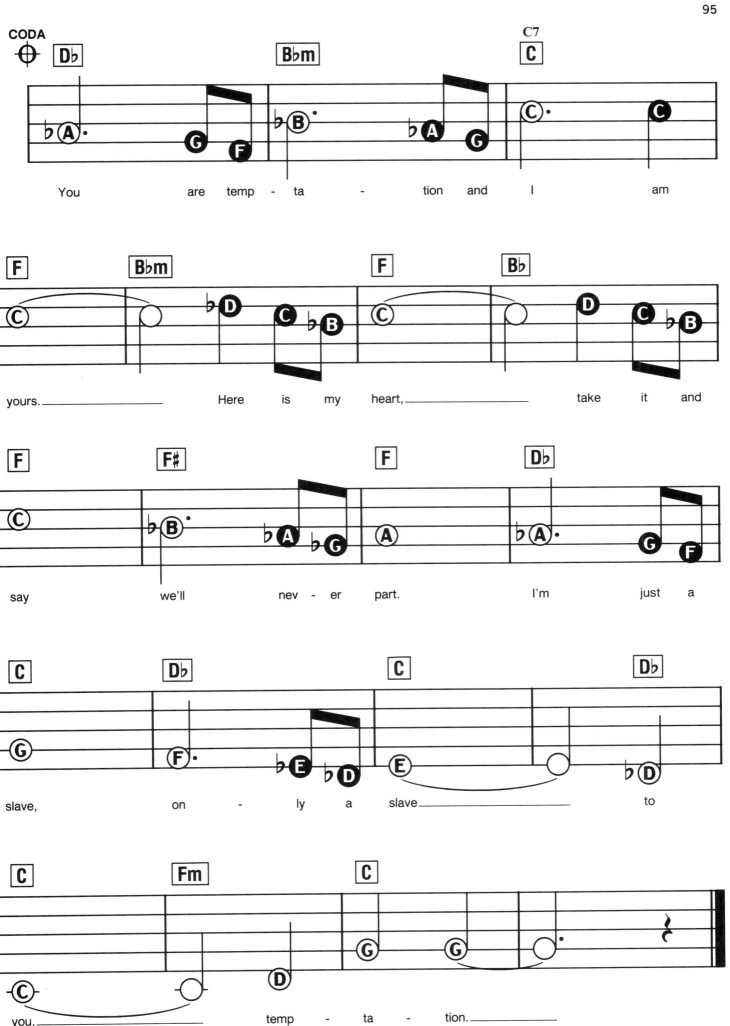

That Lucky Old Sun
(Just Rolls Around Heaven All Day)

Registration 3
Rhythm: Swing

Words by Haven Gillesp
Music by Beasley Sm

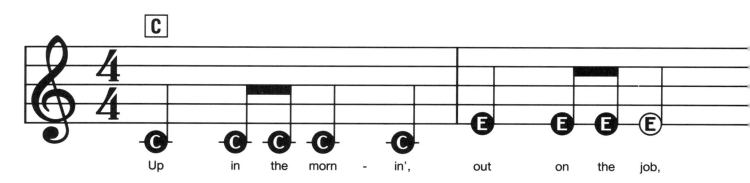

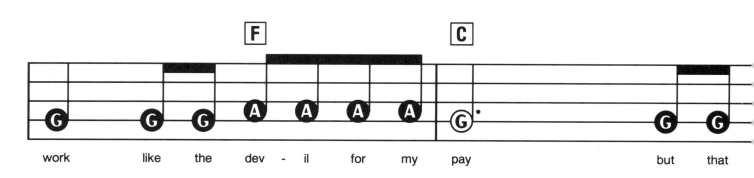

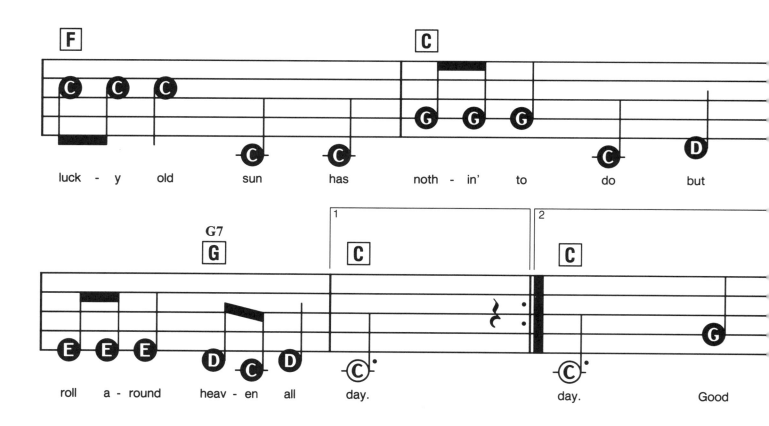

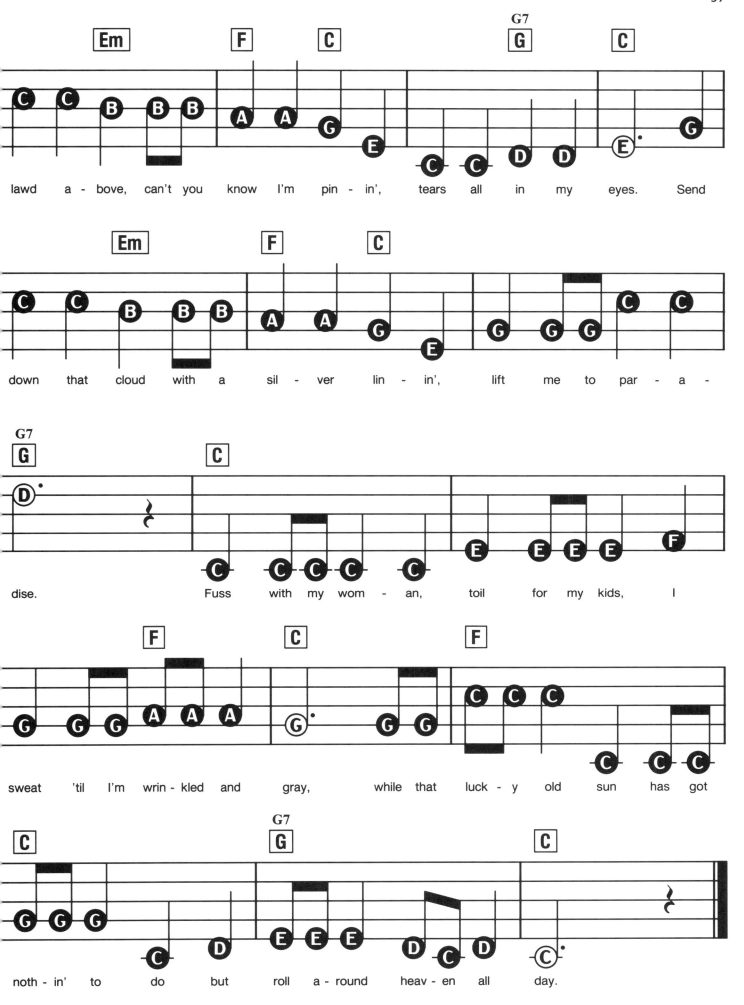

That's Amore
(From "THE CADDY")

Registration 3
Rhythm: Waltz

Words by Jack Brook
Music by Harry Warr

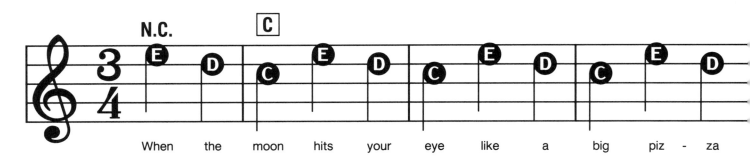

When the moon hits your eye like a big piz - za

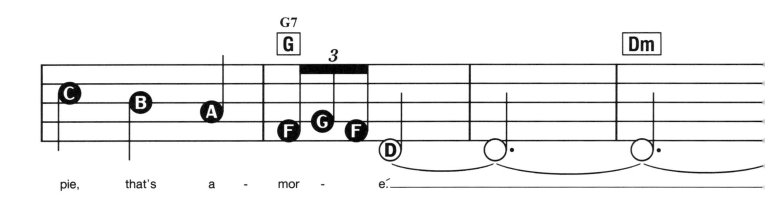

pie, that's a - mor - e.

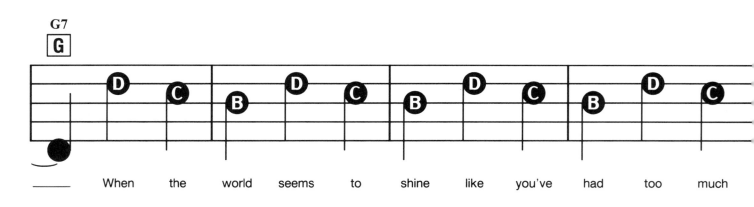

When the world seems to shine like you've had too much

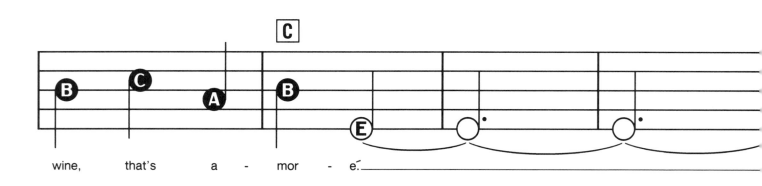

wine, that's a - mor - e.

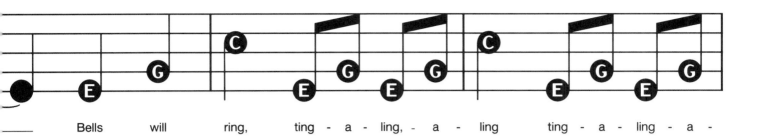

Bells will ring, ting - a - ling, - a - ling ting - a - ling - a -

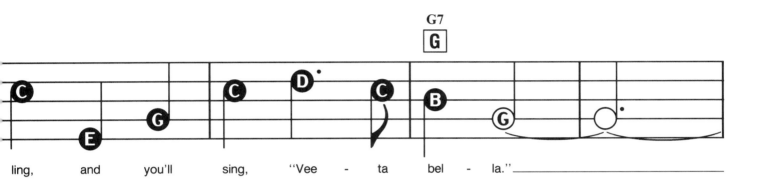

ling, and you'll sing, "Vee - ta bel - la."

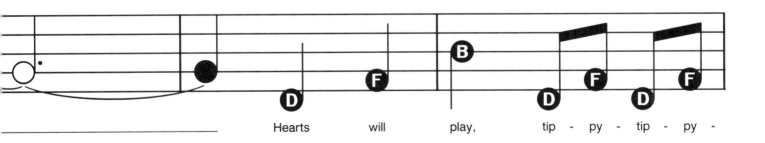

Hearts will play, tip - py - tip - py -

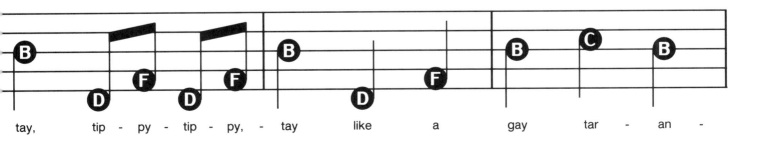

tay, tip - py - tip - py, - tay like a gay tar - an -

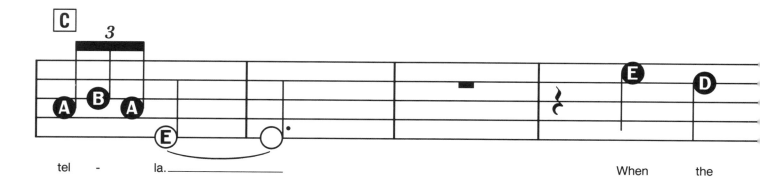

tel - la. When the

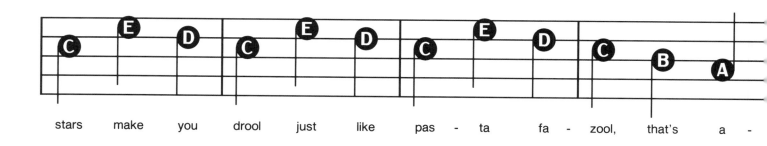

stars make you drool just like pas - ta fa - zool, that's a -

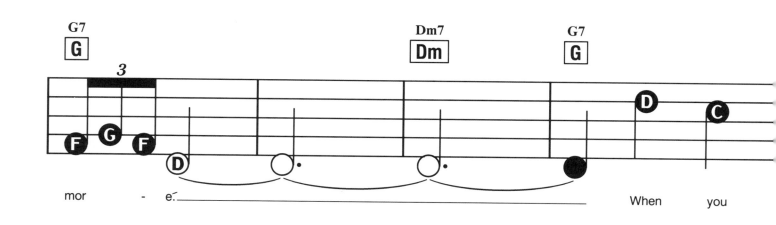

mor - e. When you

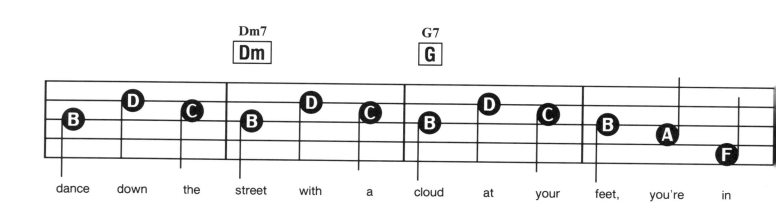

dance down the street with a cloud at your feet, you're in

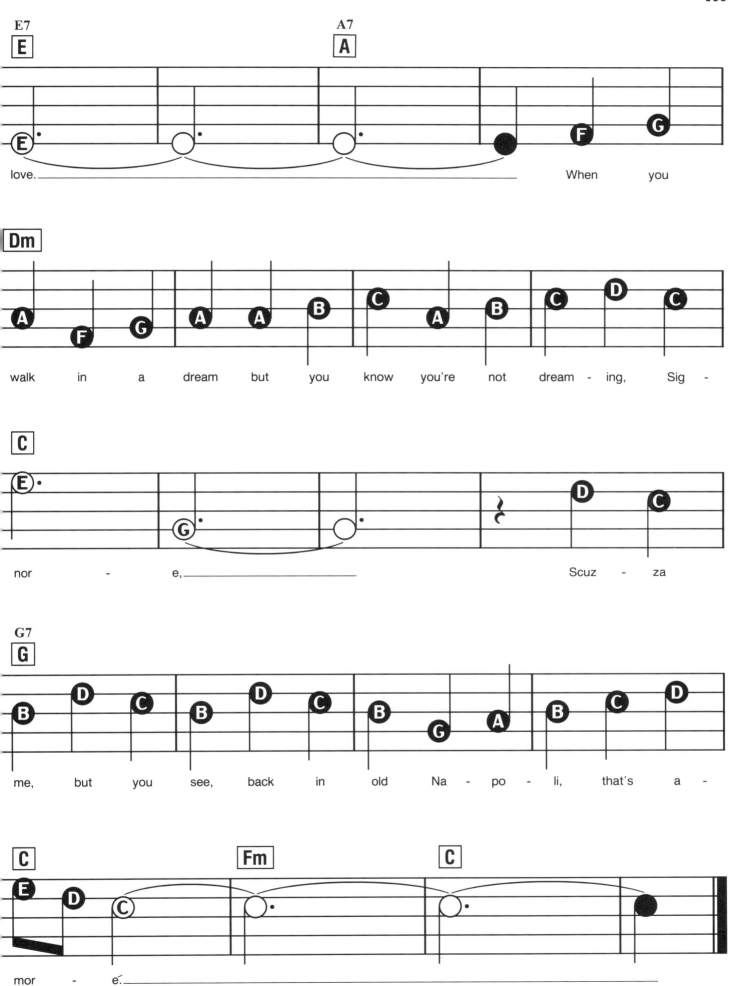

That's My Desire

Registration 2
Rhythm: Swing

Words by Carroll Loveda
Music by Helmy Kres

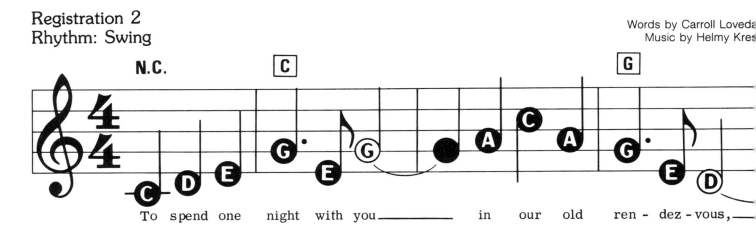

To spend one night with you____ in our old ren-dez-vous,

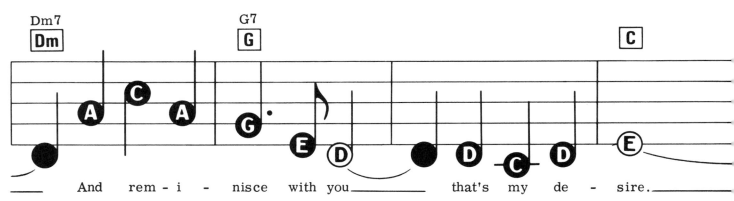

And rem-i-nisce with you____ that's my de - sire.____

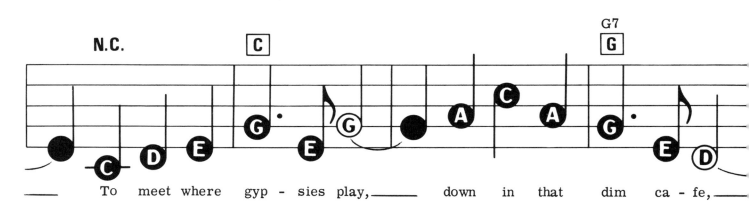

To meet where gyp-sies play,____ down in that dim ca-fe,

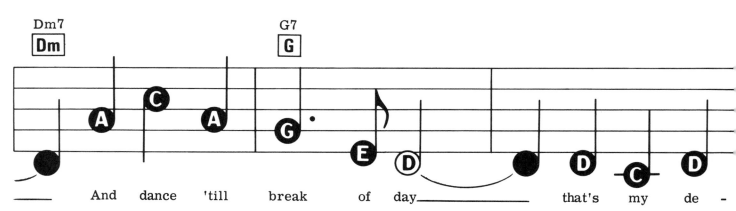

And dance 'till break of day____ that's my de -

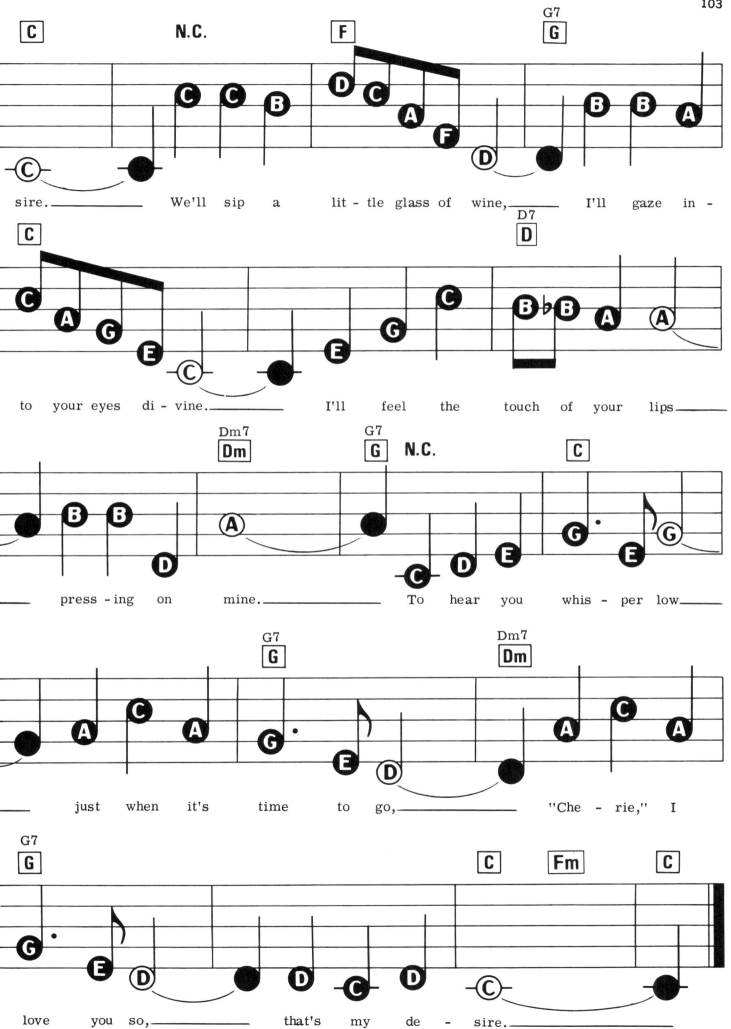

A Time For Us
(Love Theme From "ROMEO AND JULIET")

Registration 1
Rhythm: Waltz

Words by Larry Kusik and Eddie Snyd
Music by Nino Rot

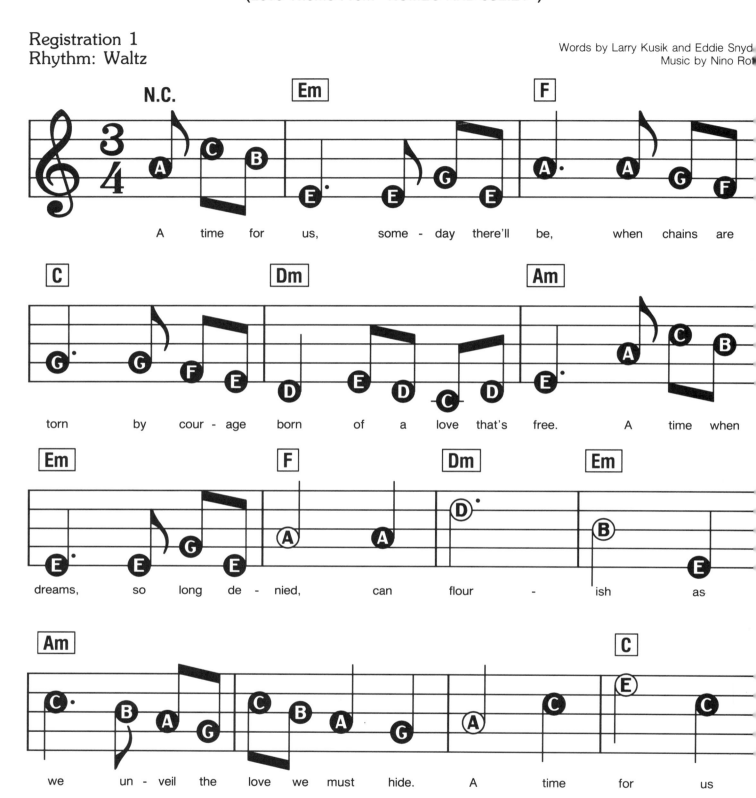

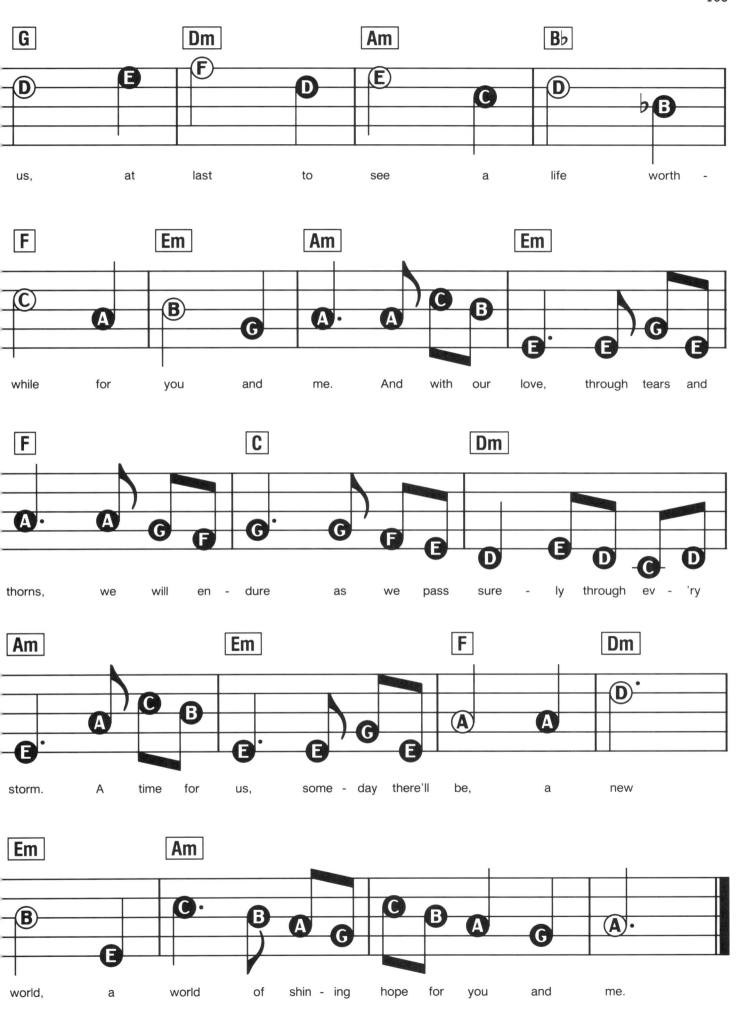

Time On My Hands

Registration 9
Rhythm: Swing

By Harold Adamson
Mack Gordon and Vincent Youman

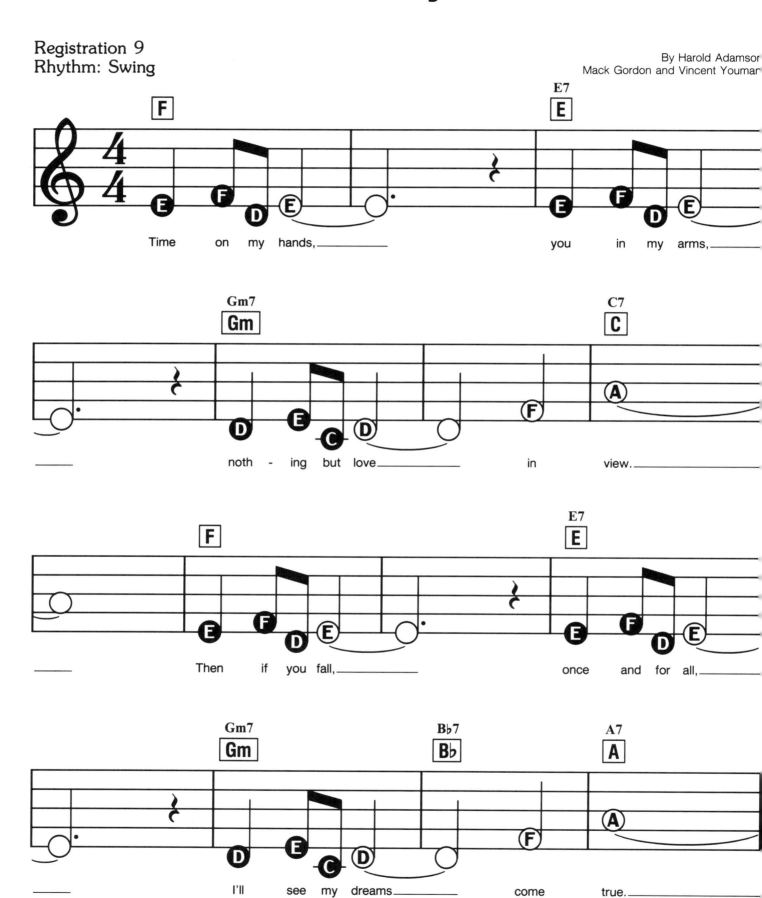

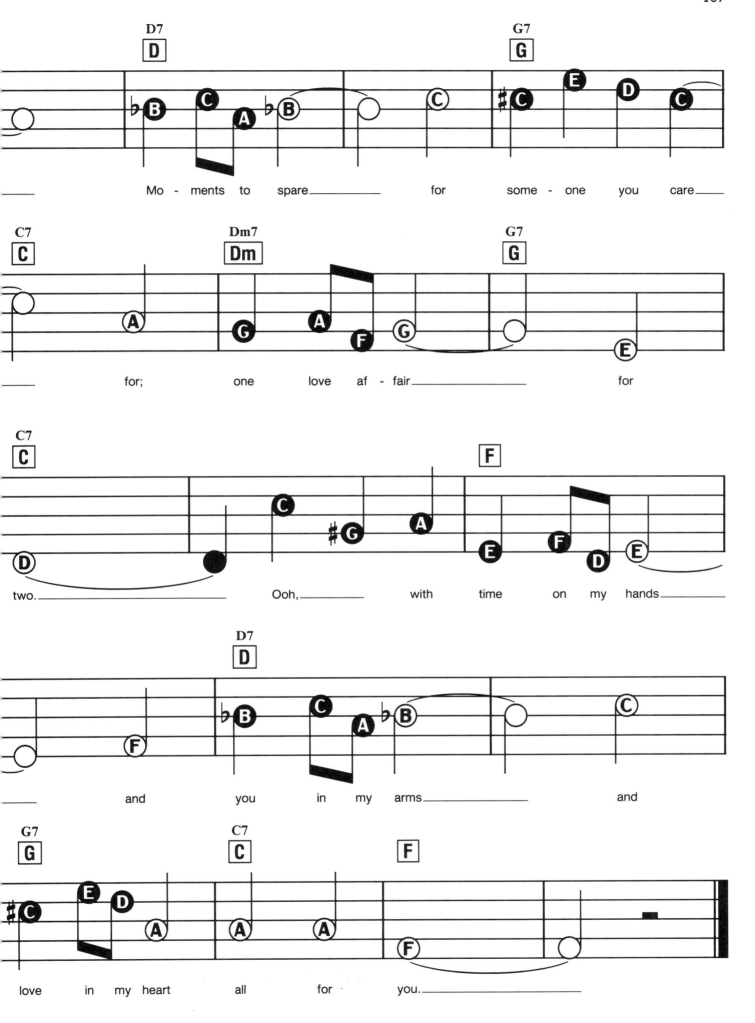

To Each His Own

Registration 2
Rhythm: Fox-Trot or Swing

By Jay Livingston
and Ray Evans

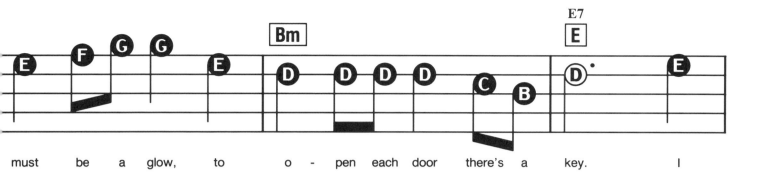

must be a glow, to o - pen each door there's a key. I

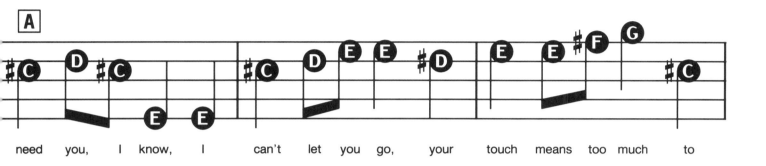

need you, I know, I can't let you go, your touch means too much to

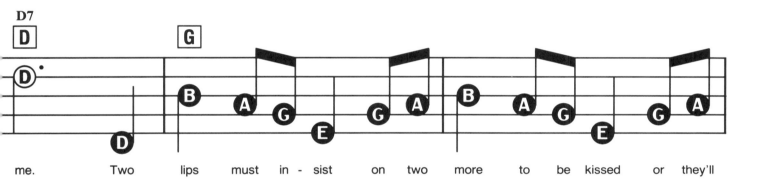

me. Two lips must in - sist on two more to be kissed or they'll

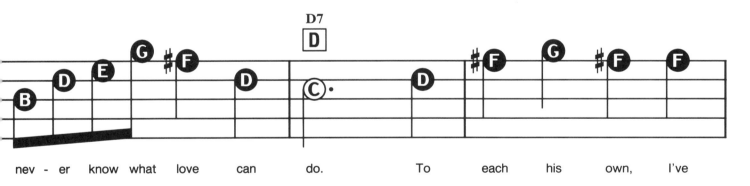

nev - er know what love can do. To each his own, I've

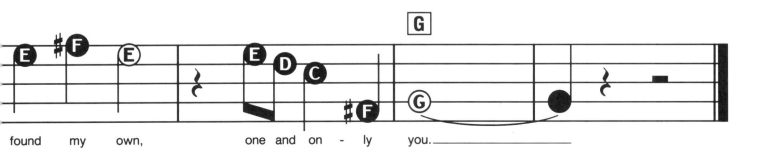

found my own, one and on - ly you.

The Trolley Song

Registration 7
Rhythm: Fox-Trot or Rock

Lyric by Hugh Mar
Music by Ralph Blar

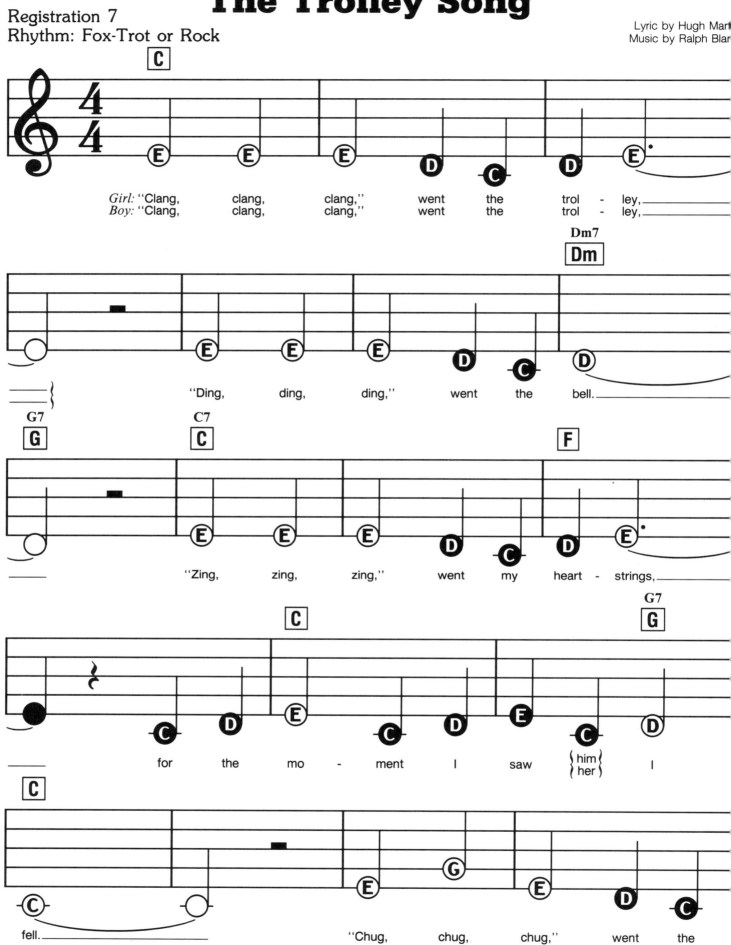

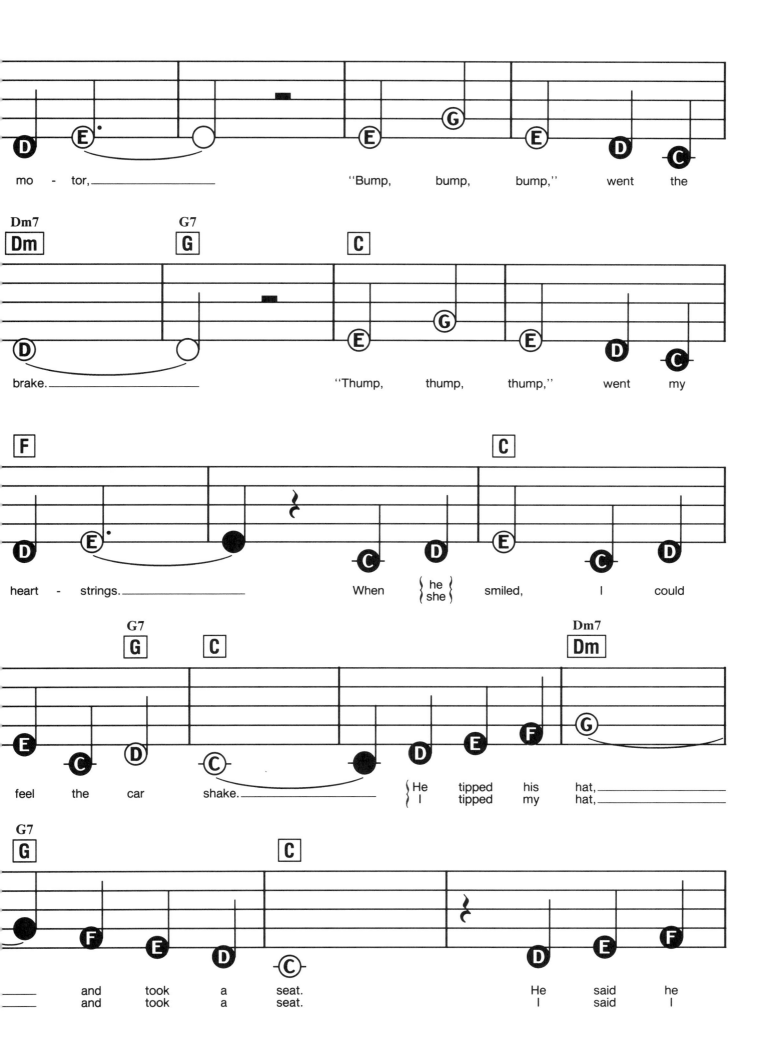

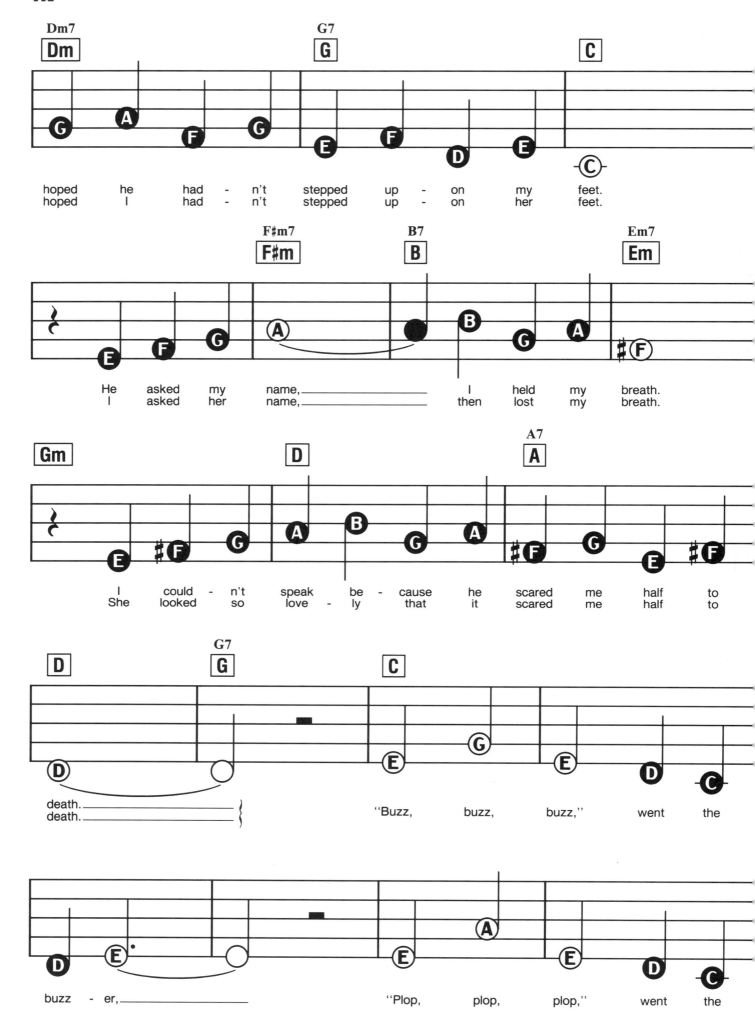

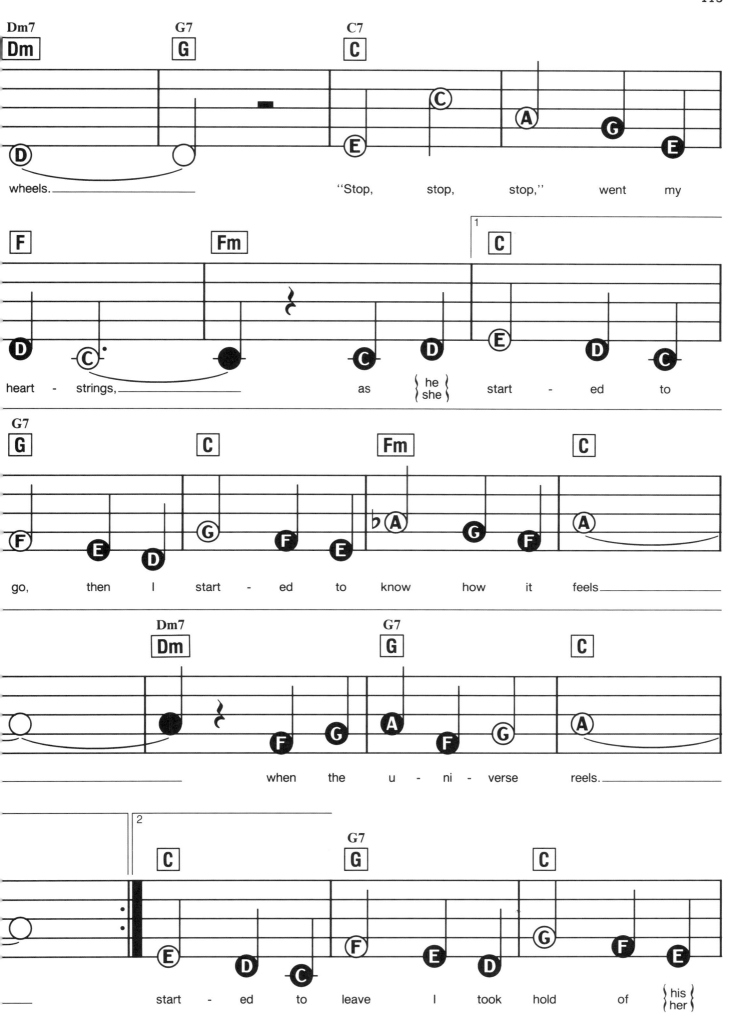

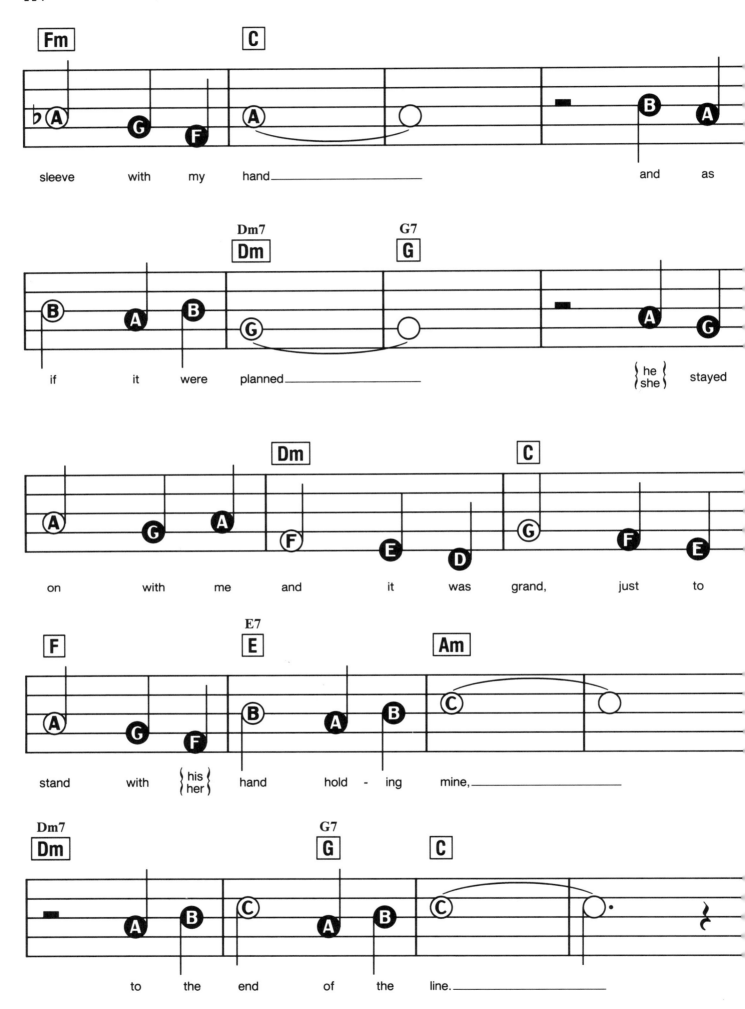

The Windmills Of Your Mind
(Theme From "THE THOMAS CROWN AFFAIR")

Registration 2
Rhythm: Rock or 8-Beat

Lyrics by Alan and Marilyn Bergman
Music by Michel Legrand

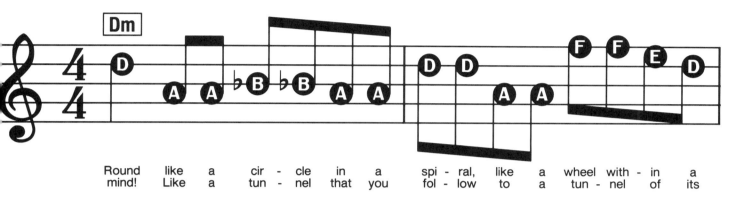

Round like a cir - cle in a spi - ral, like a wheel with - in a
mind! Like a tun - nel that you fol - low to a tun - nel of its

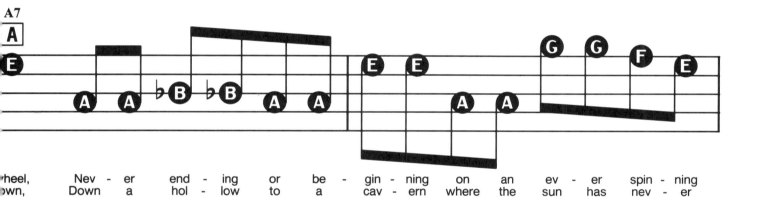

wheel, Nev - er end - ing or be - gin - ning on an ev - er spin - ning
own, Down a hol - low to a cav - ern where the sun has nev - er

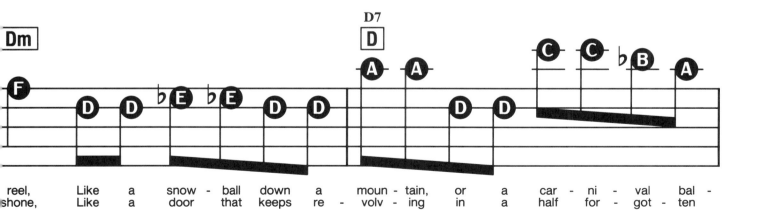

reel, Like a snow - ball down a moun - tain, or a car - ni - val bal -
shone, Like a door that keeps re - volv - ing in a half for - got - ten

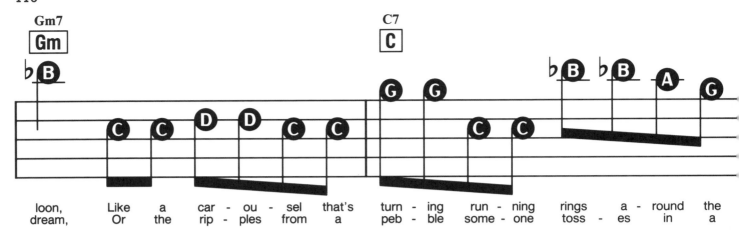

loon, Like a car - ou - sel that's turn - ing run - ning rings a - round the
dream, Or the rip - ples from a peb - ble some - one toss - es in a

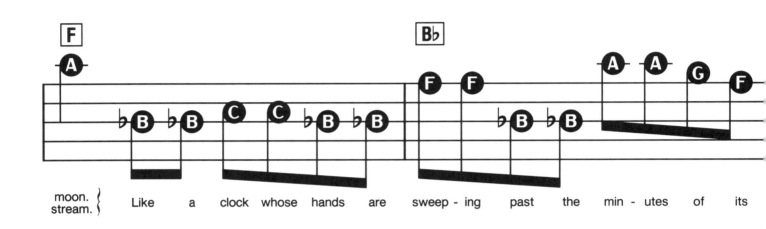

moon.
stream. Like a clock whose hands are sweep - ing past the min - utes of its

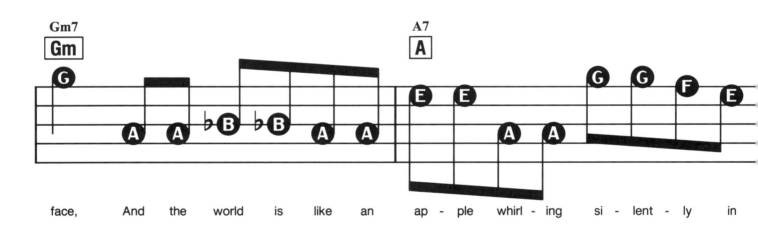

face, And the world is like an ap - ple whirl - ing si - lent - ly in

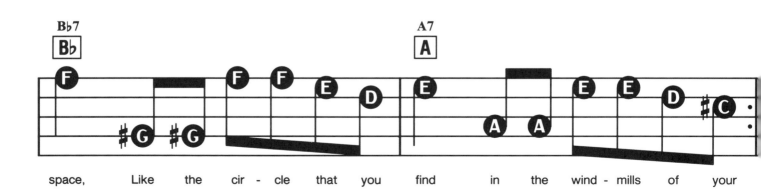

space, Like the cir - cle that you find in the wind - mills of your

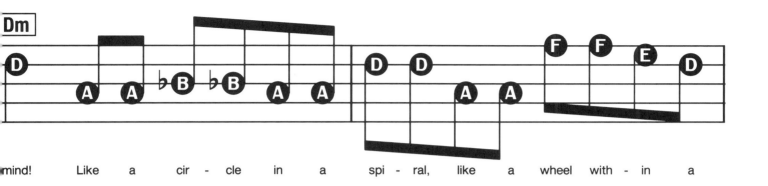

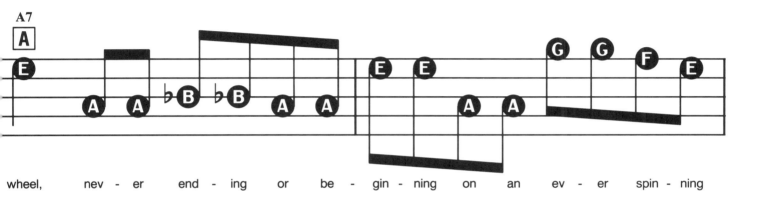

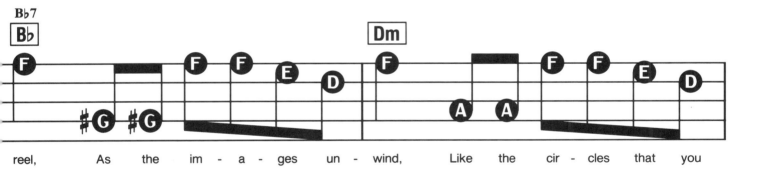

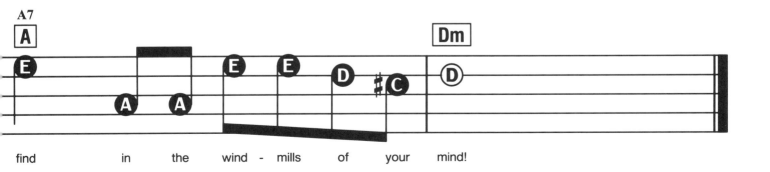

What Are You Doing The Rest Of Your Life?

Registration 2
Rhythm: Bossa or Rock

Lyrics by Alan and Marilyn Bergman
Music by Michel Legrand

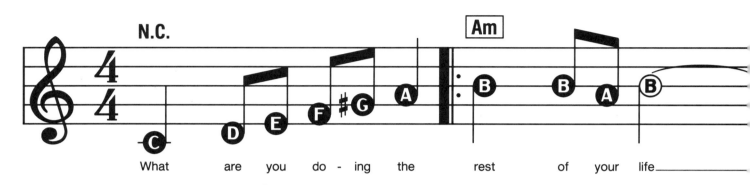

What are you do-ing the rest of your life

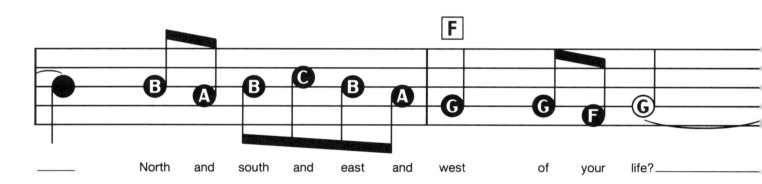

North and south and east and west of your life?

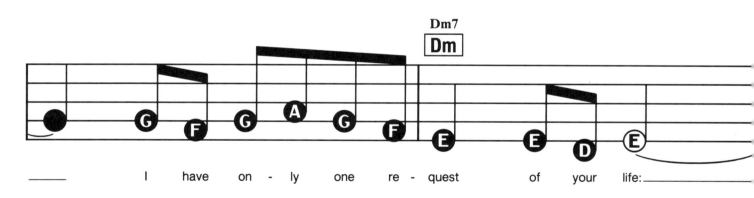

I have on-ly one re-quest of your life:

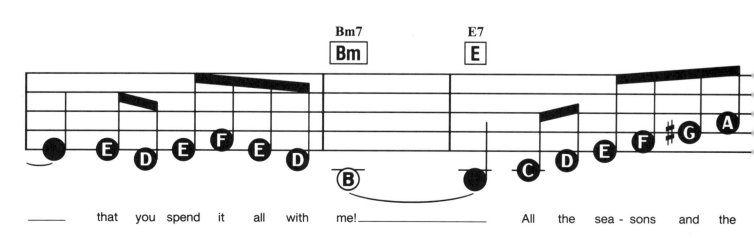

that you spend it all with me! All the sea-sons and the

119

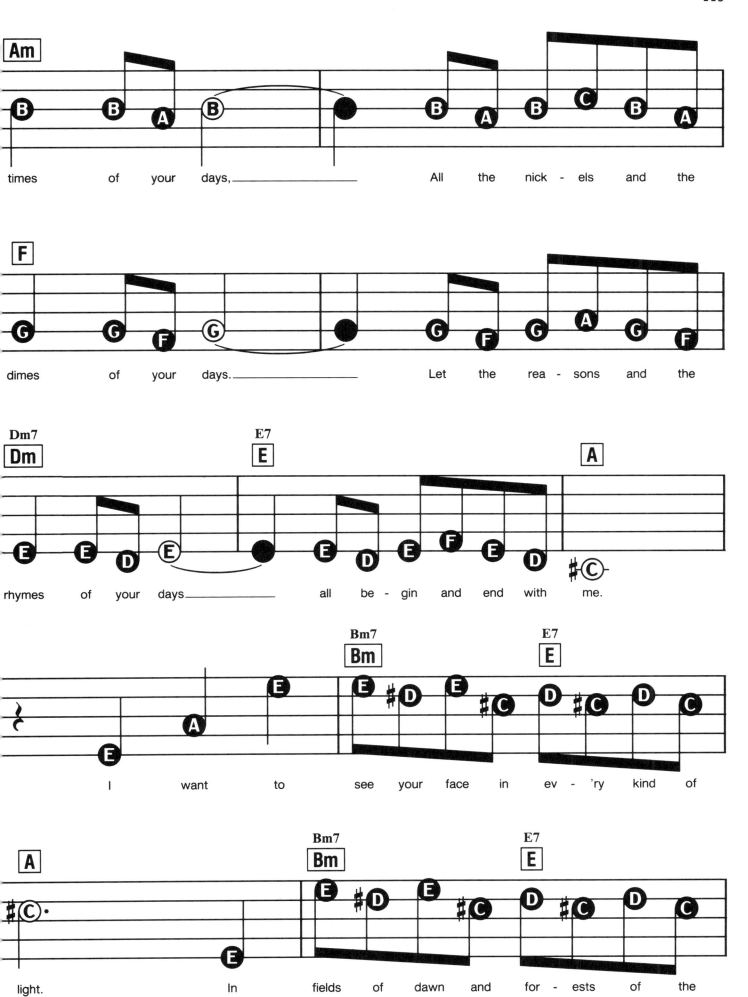

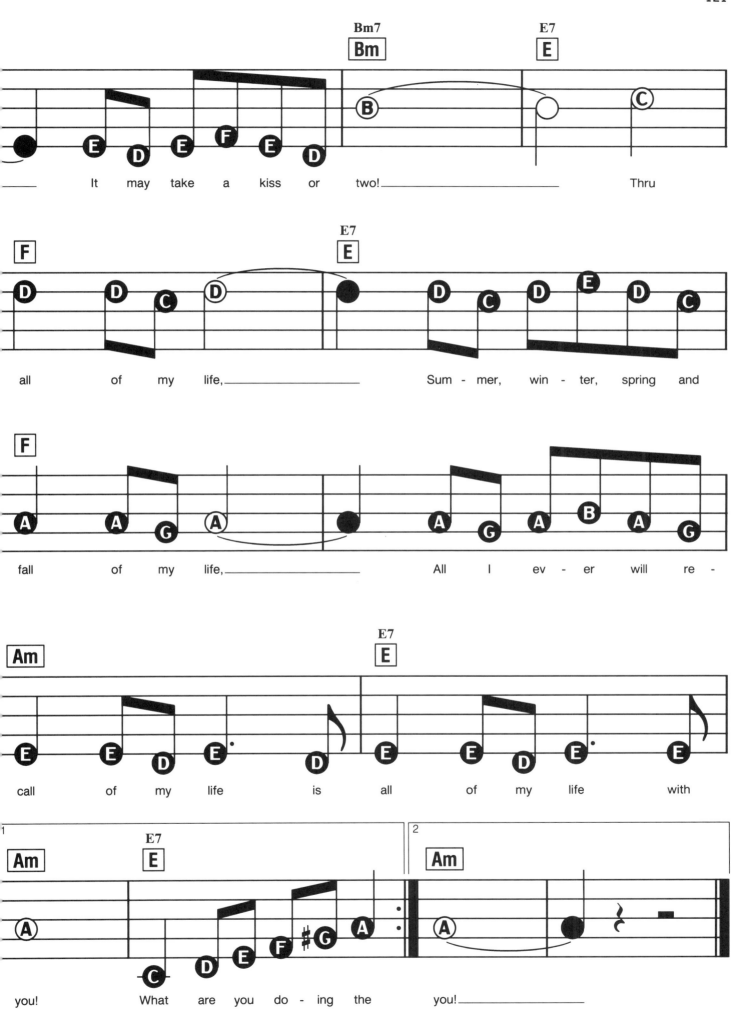

What Can I Say
After I Say I'm Sorry

Registration 4
Rhythm: Swing

Words and Music by
Walter Donaldson and Abe Lyman

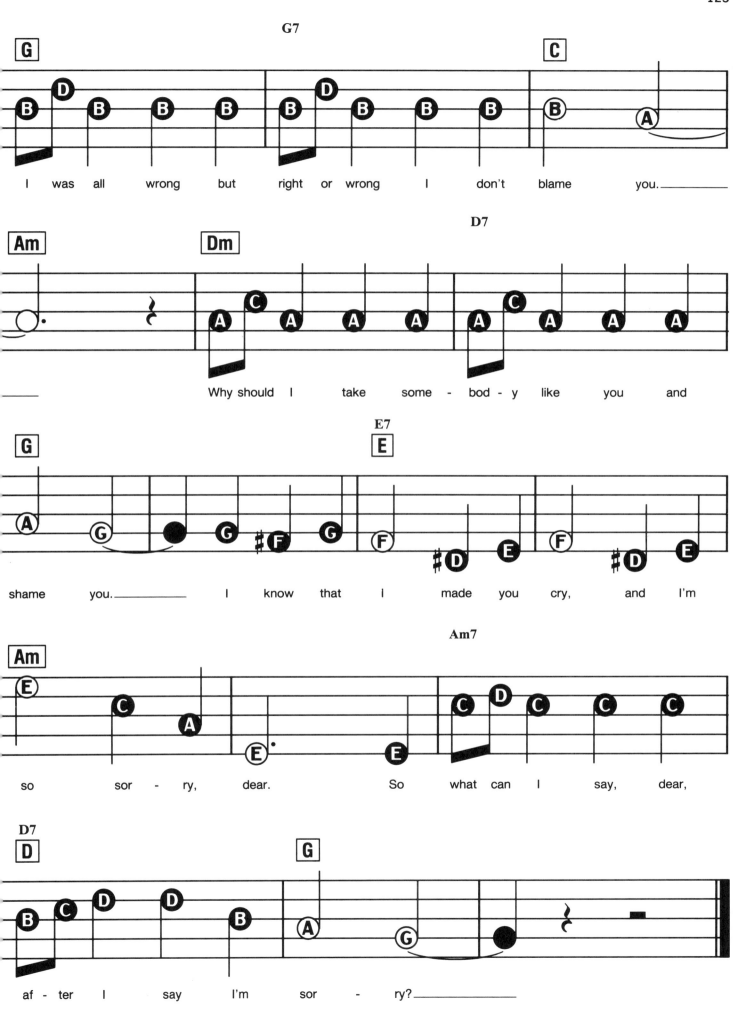

You Are So Beautiful

Registration 2
Rhythm: Pops or 8 Beat

Words and Music by
Billy Preston and Bruce Fisher

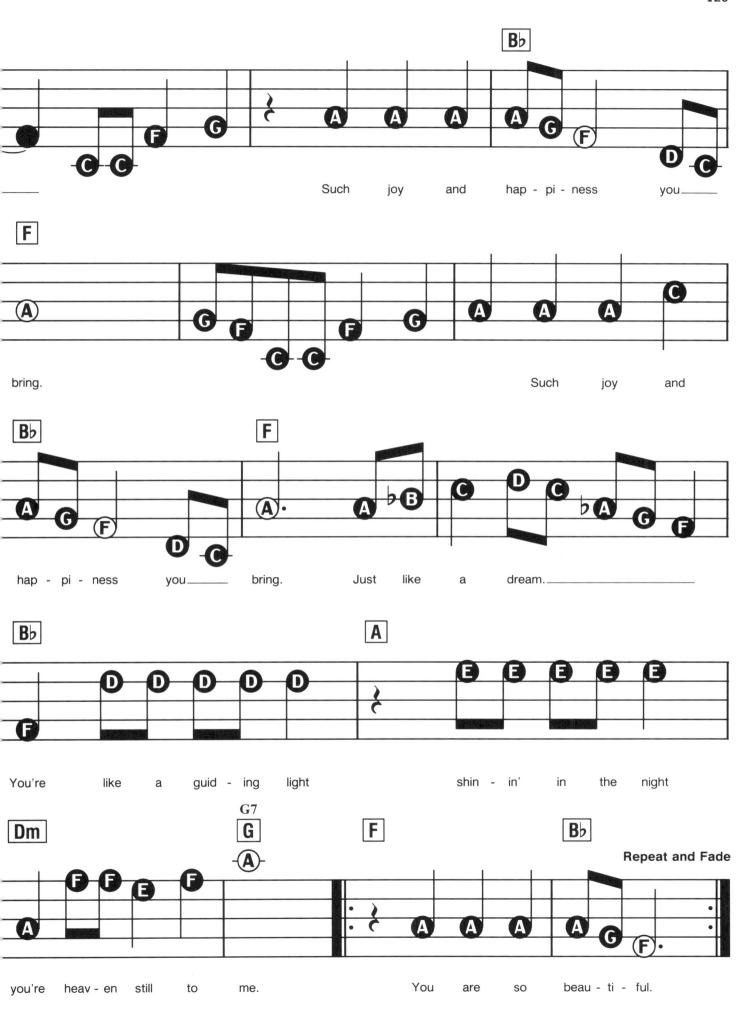

You Brought A New Kind Of Love To Me

Registration 7
Rhythm: Fox-Trot or Swing

Words and Music by Sammy Fain
Irving Kahal and Pierre Norman

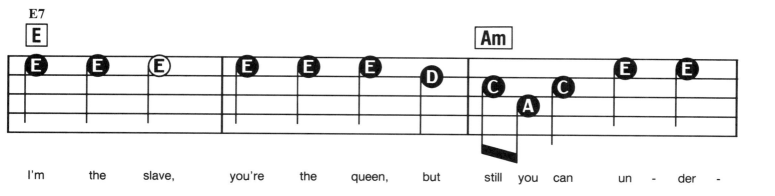

I'm   the   slave,   you're   the   queen,   but   still you can   un - der -

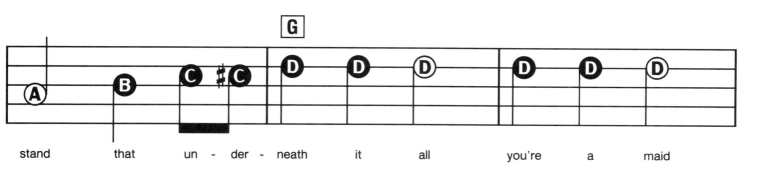

stand   that   un - der - neath   it   all   you're   a   maid

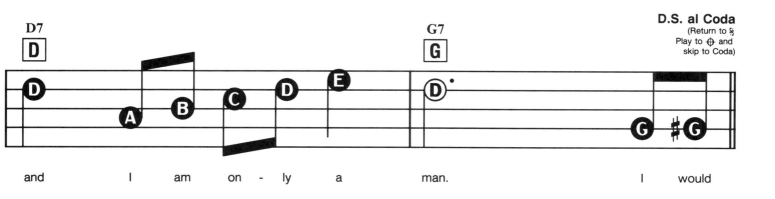

and   I   am   on - ly   a   man.   I   would

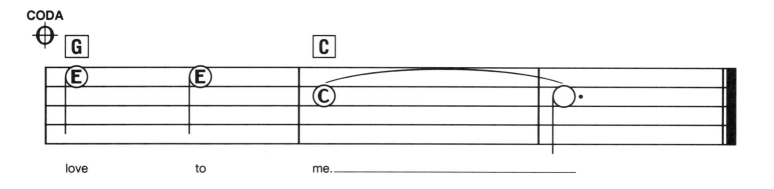

love   to   me.

Registration Guide

- Match the Registration number on the song to the corresponding numbered category below. Select and activate an instrumental sound available on your instrument.

- Choose an automatic rhythm appropriate to the mood and style of the song. (Consult your Owner's Guide for proper operation of automatic rhythm features.)

- Adjust the tempo and volume controls to comfortable settings.

Registration

1	Flute, Pan Flute, Jazz Flute
2	Clarinet, Organ
3	Violin, Strings
4	Brass, Trumpet
5	Synth Ensemble, Accordion, Brass
6	Pipe Organ, Harpsichord
7	Jazz Organ, Vibraphone, Vibes, Electric Piano, Jazz Guitar
8	Piano, Electric Piano
9	Trumpet, Trombone, Clarinet, Saxophone, Oboe
10	Violin, Cello, Strings